# Developing Nu

## SOLVING PROBLEMS

### ACTIVITIES FOR THE DAILY MATHS LESSON

# year

# 6

## Hilary Koll and Steve Mills

## A & C BLACK

# Contents

## Problems involving money

## Problems involving measures

## Answers

Reprinted 2001, 2002 (twice), 2004, 2005
Published 2000 by A & C Black Publishers Limited
37 Soho Square, London W1D 3QZ
www.acblack.com

ISBN 0-7136-5449-X

The authors and publishers would like to thank the following teachers for their advice in producing this series of books:
Stuart Anslow; Jane Beynon; Cathy Davey; Ann Flint; Shirley Gooch; Barbara Locke; Madeleine Madden; Helen Mason;
Fern Oliver; Jo Turpin.

A CIP catalogue record for this book is available from the British Library.

A & C Black uses paper produced with elemental chlorine-free pulp, harvested from managed sustainable forests.

Printed and bound in Great Britain by Cromwell Press Ltd, Trowbridge.

# Introduction

**Developing Numeracy: Solving Problems** is a series of seven photocopiable activity books designed to be used during the daily maths lesson. It focuses on the third strand of the National Numeracy Strategy *Framework for teaching mathematics*. The activities are intended to be used in the time allocated to pupil activities; they aim to reinforce the knowledge, understanding and skills taught during the main part of the lesson and to provide practice and consolidation of the objectives contained in the framework document.

**Year 6** supports the teaching of mathematics by providing a series of activities which develop essential skills in solving mathematical problems. On the whole the activities are designed for children to work on independently, although this is not always possible and occasionally some children may need support.

**Year 6** encourages children to

- choose and use appropriate number operations to solve problems and to use appropriate ways of calculating;
- solve mathematical problems and puzzles and to explore relationships and patterns;
- investigate a general statement about familiar numbers or shapes;
- express a generalised relationship as a formula;
- explain their methods and reasoning;
- solve one-step and multi-step worded problems in areas of 'real life', money and measures;
- convert foreign currency to pounds, and vice versa and to calculate fractions and percentages.

## Extension

Many of the activity sheets end with a challenge (**Now try this!**) which reinforces and extends the children's learning, and provides the teacher with the opportunity for assessment. On occasions you may wish to read out the instructions and explain the activity before the children begin working on it. The children may need to record their answers on a separate piece of paper.

## Differentiated activities

For some activities, two differentiated versions are provided which have the same title and are presented on facing pages in the book. On the left is the less challenging activity, indicated by a rocket icon: . The more challenging version is found on the right, indicated by a shooting star: . These activity sheets could be given to different groups within the class, or all the children could complete the first sheet and children requiring further extension could then be given the second sheet.

## Organisation

Very little equipment is needed, but it will be useful to have available: coloured pencils, interlocking cubes, scissors, digit cards, dice, dominoes, squared paper and protractors. You will need to provide a teaspoon, tablespoon and pint jug for page 55 and television schedules for pages 58 and 59, if desired.

Where calculators should be used, this is indicated on the page; otherwise it is left to the teacher's discretion.

To help teachers to select appropriate learning experiences for the children, the activities are grouped into sections within each book. However, the activities are not expected to be used in that order unless otherwise stated. The sheets are intended to support, rather than direct, the teacher's planning.

Some activities can be made easier or more challenging by masking and substituting some of the numbers. You may wish to re-use some pages by copying them onto card and laminating them, or by enlarging them onto A3 paper.

## Teachers' notes

Brief notes are provided at the foot of each page giving ideas and suggestions for maximising the effectiveness of the activity sheets. These can be masked before copying.

## Structure of the daily maths lesson

The recommended structure of the daily maths lesson for Key Stage 2 is as follows:

| | |
|---|---|
| Start to lesson, oral work, mental calculation | 5–10 minutes |
| Main teaching and pupil activities *(the activities in the **Developing Numeracy** books are designed to be carried out in the time allocated to pupil activities)* | about 40 minutes |
| Plenary *(whole-class review and consolidation)* | about 10 minutes |

# Whole-class activities

The following activities provide some practical ideas which can be used to introduce or reinforce the main teaching part of the lesson.

## Making decisions

### Stand up

Choose two children to stand up and face each other. One of the children should say a whole number, fraction or decimal, and the other child should say an operation, for example *add*. Give them a second number, taking care to make the question simple enough for the class to perform. The rest of the class must try to work out the answer. If they do so within an allocated time, the pair sit down and two more children are chosen. Children may choose very large numbers initially, but your questions might include '÷ 1', 'x 1', '+ 1' or '– 1' so that the question is, in fact, easy to solve. Children will begin to realise that suggesting numbers and signs such as '37' and '–' or '179' and 'x' can result in harder questions.

### Number question strip

On a strip of card or thick paper write a number fact, for example *521 + 455 = 976*. Wrap a narrow piece of paper around the strip of card so that it can slide sideways to mask one of the numbers or operator signs. Hold up the strip and ask the children to find the hidden number or sign. This can then be revealed to check that it is correct. You could build up a collection of number strips to use throughout the year.

## Reasoning about numbers

### Counting stick

You will need a stick which is divided into ten equal coloured sections (such as a metre stick with each 10 cm coloured). Hold the stick so that all the children can see it and point to each section along it in turn. Decide on a number (for example, nine) and ask the children to count in nines as you point to each section. This provides practice in counting forwards and backwards and helps the children to remember the multiples of the given number.

## Reasoning about shapes

### Diagonals

Discuss the meaning of the word 'diagonal' in the context of 2-D shapes. Draw simple rectangles and other quadrilaterals on the board and explore the diagonal properties. Ask the children:
*Which shapes have diagonals that meet at right angles?*
*Are diagonals of all quadrilaterals equal in length?*
*Name the shapes which have equal length diagonals.*

After exploring quadrilaterals, discuss other shapes such as triangles (no diagonals) and other types of regular polygons.

## Problems involving 'real life'

### Football tables

Photocopy a set of football tables and explain to the children how they work. Mask some of the numbers on the table and then ask questions such as:
*How many points do you think Spurs have?*
*How many times have Leeds United won if they have 33 points and have drawn only twice?*
*If Arsenal and Chelsea play each other, how could this affect the table?*

## Problems involving money

### Shopping trip

Draw five items on the board with price labels, for example £1.75, 48p, £1.99, £2.20, 83p. Ask the children to work out the total cost for three or more items. Choose a child to ask a question in the following way:
*I went shopping and bought three things. I paid £X. What did I buy?*
The rest of the class should try to work out the items bought.

## Problems involving measures

### Time zones

Show the children a map with time zones on it and explain how the time zones work. Ask the children to choose a place marked on the map, and together work out what time it is in that place at, for example, 10:00. Compile a class list of times in different places at 10:00. You could ask individual children to stand up and declare the time and place.

# Decimal detectives

The decimal points have vanished from two numbers in each number statement.

- Write the missing points to make each statement correct. One has been done for you.

**1.**
96·9 − 9·03 = 87·87

**2.**
4604 − 725 = 387·9

**3.**
3051 × 31 = 945·81

**4.**
606 ÷ 404 = 0·15

**5.**
2854 + 364 = 289·04

**6.**
143 × 974 = 139·282

**7.**
10000 ÷ 80 = 0·125

**8.**
1229 + 983 = 221·2

**9.**
3003 × 984 = 2954·952

- Place decimal points anywhere in this question and work out the answer.

28403 + 352 =

- Try it again. Make as many answers as you can.

**Teachers' note** Encourage the children to make approximations, for example, 'The answer is about 100, so the numbers in front of the decimal point must add up to make about 100.'

**Developing Numeracy**
**Solving Problems Year 6**
© A & C Black

# Decimal stories

- **Make up a number story for each number statement.**

  **Use** g and kg , cm, m and km , ml and l **or** £ and p .

  Example: $0.27 \times 24 = 6.48$

  A doughnut costs 27p. 24 doughnuts cost £6.48.

---

**1.** $124.3 + 36.44 = 160.74$

_____

_____

_____

_____

**2.** $448.91 \div 53 = 8.47$

_____

_____

_____

_____

**3.** $58.72 - 17.5 = 41.22$

_____

_____

_____

_____

**4.** $264.5 - 2.99 = 261.51$

_____

_____

_____

_____

**5.** $38.4 \div 8 = 4.8$

_____

_____

_____

_____

**6.** $23.7 \times 15 = 355.5$

_____

_____

_____

_____

---

**Now try this!**

- **Write three more number statements.**
- **Ask a partner to write matching number stories.**

---

**Teachers' note** The instruction, worked example and one number in each statement can be masked before photocopying to create missing number statements. The number stories can then be written as number questions for a partner to solve.

Developing Numeracy
Solving Problems Year 6
© A & C Black

# Unravel the riddle

- **Work out which numbers the star and circle stand for.**

The star is always the same value.

The circle is always the same value.

$$\star + \bigcirc = 24 \qquad \star - \bigcirc = 20$$

$$\bigcirc + \star = 24 \qquad \bigcirc - \star = -20$$

$$\star \times \bigcirc = 44 \qquad \star \div \bigcirc = 11$$

$$\bigcirc \times \star = 44 \qquad \bigcirc \div \star = 0.090909$$

$$\star = \underline{\qquad} \qquad \bigcirc = \underline{\qquad}$$

- **Work out which numbers the square and triangle stand for.**

The square is always the same value.

The triangle is always the same value.

$$\square + \triangle = 45 \qquad \square - \triangle = -27$$

$$\triangle + \square = 45 \qquad \triangle - \square = 27$$

$$\square \times \triangle = 324 \qquad \square \div \triangle = 0.25$$

$$\triangle \times \square = 324 \qquad \triangle \div \square = 4$$

$$\square = \underline{\qquad} \qquad \triangle = \underline{\qquad}$$

- **Work out which numbers A and B stand for.**

Now try this!

$$A + B = 19 \qquad A - B = -1 \qquad A = \underline{\qquad}$$
$$B + A = 19 \qquad B - A = 1$$
$$A \times B = 90 \qquad A \div B = 0.9 \qquad B = \underline{\qquad}$$
$$B \times A = 90 \qquad B \div A = 1.1111111$$

**Teachers' note** Ensure that the children realise that the symbols stand for the same value in all the number statements in each section. Provide children with calculators to help them investigate.

**Developing Numeracy
Solving Problems Year 6
© A & C Black**

8

# Unravel the riddle

- **Work out which numbers A and B stand for in each section.**

**1.**

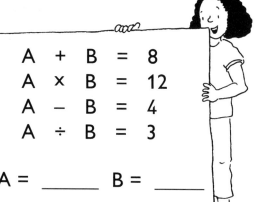

A + B = 8
A × B = 12
A − B = 4
A ÷ B = 3

A = _____   B = _____

**2.**

A + B = 20
A × B = 96
A − B = 4
A ÷ B = 1·5

A = _____   B = _____

**3.**

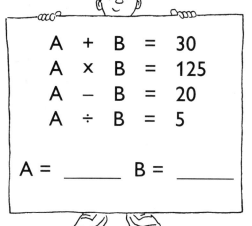

A + B = 30
A × B = 125
A − B = 20
A ÷ B = 5

A = _____   B = _____

**4.**

A + B = 14
A × B = 45
A − B = -4
A ÷ B = 0·5555

A = _____   B = _____

---

**A, B, C, D, E and F stand for the digits** ⌐1 to 6⌐.

- **Work out which digit each letter stands for.**

A + A = B          A × D = F          D × E = C E

C + C = A          B × F = A B        E × E = A E

F − E = C          C × F = F          D × B = C A

A = ___   B = ___   C = ___   D = ___   E = ___   F = ___

---

**Teachers' note** Ensure that the children realise that these are codes where one letter stands for a digit, rather than an algebraic equation, for example, AB is a different two-digit number from BA. For the extension activity, the children could be provided with 1 to 6 digit cards to rearrange practically.

**Developing Numeracy
Solving Problems Year 6
© A & C Black**

# Virus attack

**Uh-oh! A virus has erased some digits from Zack's computer.**

• **Write the missing digits.**

Use a calculator to help you.

1. ⬚1 ⬚0 ⬚2 × 5⬚9 = 6 018

2. ⬚ ⬚ ⬚ × 3⬚ = 6 142

3. ⬚ ⬚ ⬚ × 4⬚ = 10 212

4. 1 ⬚ ⬚ × ⬚4 = 9 936

5. 7 ⬚ ⬚ × ⬚3 = 74 307

6. 7 ⬚ ⬚ × ⬚3 = 9 243

7. ⬚ ⬚6 × ⬚6 = 8 736

8. ⬚9 × ⬚ ⬚ = 779

9. ⬚4 × ⬚ ⬚ = 7 568

• **Find as many ways as you can to complete this.**

☐ + ☐ + ☐ = 0·1

Example: 0·01 + 0·01 + 0·08 = 0·1

**Teachers' note** Discuss how to solve calculator puzzles by looking for clues in the numbers given, for example, deciding whether it will be a large digit or a small digit, and then inserting digits and testing them. Encourage the children to use their knowledge of inverses to work backwards from the answer.

**Developing Numeracy
Solving Problems Year 6
© A & C Black**

# Work it out

• **Work out the answers.**

Show your workings.

**1.** 42 × 25 =

**2.** 384 ÷ 8 =

**3.** $\frac{1}{5}$ of 400 =

**4.** 224 ÷ 12 =

**5.** 15% of 240 =

**6.** 35 × 56 =

**7.** 354 ÷ 9 =

Now try this!

• **Explain in words how you would work out** 17·5% **of a number.**

**Teachers' note** The children could give answers to division questions using a whole number remainder, a fractional remainder or by writing the answer as a decimal number, for example, 21 r 2, 21 $\frac{2}{3}$, or 21·6666. Note that some questions involve recurring decimals.

**Developing Numeracy
Solving Problems Year 6
© A & C Black**

# Domino shuffle

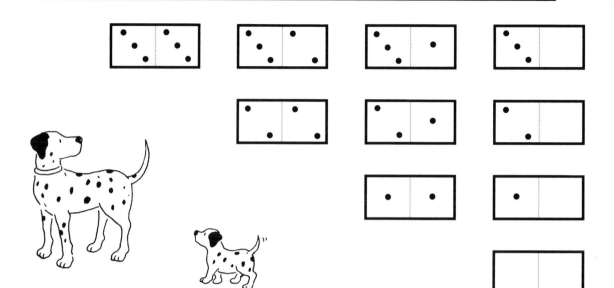

These dominoes can be arranged so that the total number of spots in each <u>row</u> is ⌐15⌐ and the total in each <u>column</u> is ⌐3⌐.

• Draw spots to show how you can do this.

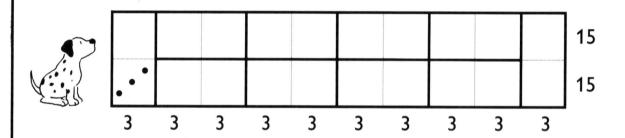

If the [⋰.⋰] domino is taken away, the other dominoes can be arranged so that the total number of spots in each <u>row</u> is ⌐8⌐ and the total in each <u>column</u> is ⌐4⌐.

• Draw spots to show how you can do this.

 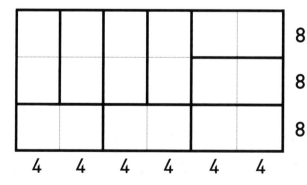 

**Teachers' note** Some children may benefit from having the dominoes in front of them to arrange practically. The children might prefer to record the dominoes using numbers rather than spots, for example 2:3. Remind the children that only nine dominoes are used for the second activity.

Developing Numeracy
Solving Problems Year 6
© A & C Black

12

• **Play this game with a partner. You will need a cube.**

☆ Place the cube on any dot to start the game.

☆ Player 1 begins with the number 100 and follows the instruction. Example: 100 → find 80% = 80

☆ Player 2 begins with this number and moves the cube to another dot. They follow the instruction. Example: 80 → subtract 16 = 64

☆ Carry on taking turns to move the cube.

☆ All your answers must be whole numbers!

• **How many turns can you take before you have to give an answer that is not a whole number?**

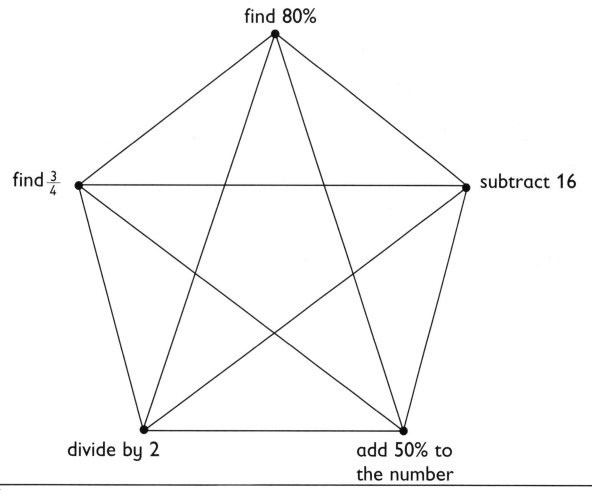

find 80%

find $\frac{3}{4}$

subtract 16

divide by 2

add 50% to the number

• **Start with the number** 100 .

• **On your own, find a route that takes you to** 1 .

**Teachers' note** Tell the children that a five-pointed star is called a 'pentacle'; 'pent' coming from the Greek word for five, as in 'pentagon', 'pentomino', etc. The instructions at each point can be masked before photocopying, and others inserted, to create a flexible resource. Note that children can use negative and positive whole numbers (integers).

**Developing Numeracy
Solving Problems Year 6
© A & C Black**

# Next-door neighbours

In this hotel, the doors are numbered consecutively from |1 to 50|.

• **Look at these two doors.**

5 and 6 are consecutive numbers.

**The product of the numbers is** |30|.

5 × 6 = 30

• **Which consecutive numbers are on these pairs of doors?**

**Look at the product of the two numbers.**

product = 42

product = 72

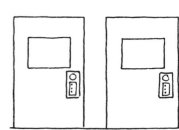

product = 110

product = 210

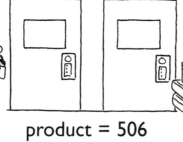

product = 506

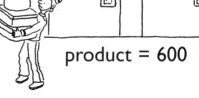

product = 600

product = 812

product = 1190

product = 2450

• **Write all the pairs of consecutive numbers which have a product between** |100| **and** |200|.

**Teachers' note** Revise the meanings of the words 'consecutive' and 'product'. Provide calculators for this activity and encourage the children to look for clues, for example, the product ends in a zero, so one number might be a multiple of 5 or 10.

**Developing Numeracy
Solving Problems Year 6
© A & C Black**

# Next-door neighbours

In this hotel, the doors are numbered consecutively from  1 to 100 .

- **Look at these two doors.**

    5 and 6 are consecutive numbers.

    **The product of the numbers is  30 .**

    5 × 6 = 30

- **Which consecutive numbers are on these pairs of doors?**

    **Look at the product of the two numbers.**

product = 156          product = 240

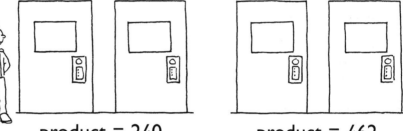

product = 462

product = 756          product = 1122

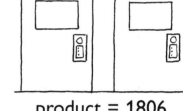

product = 1806

product = 4422          product = 6806          product = 9900

**Now try this!**

- **Write all the pairs of consecutive numbers which have a product between  500  and  1000 .**

**Teachers' note** Revise the meanings of the words 'consecutive' and 'product'. Provide calculators for this activity and encourage the children to look for clues, for example, the product ends in a zero, so one number might be a multiple of 5 or 10.

**Developing Numeracy
Solving Problems Year 6
© A & C Black**

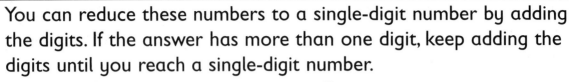

# Rapid reducing: 1

You can reduce these numbers to a single-digit number by adding the digits. If the answer has more than one digit, keep adding the digits until you reach a single-digit number.

26 → ⑧         29 → 11 → ②

• **Which single-digit number do these reduce to in** [one] **step?**

71 → ◯         63 → ◯         13 → ◯         44 → ◯

81 → ◯         72 → ◯         62 → ◯         53 → ◯

• **Which single-digit number do these reduce to in** [two] **steps?**

46 → → ◯         57 → → ◯         98 → → ◯

88 → → ◯         75 → → ◯         99 → → ◯

• **On the 100-square, colour yellow all the two-digit or three-digit numbers that reduce to a single digit in** [one] **step.**

| 1 | 2 | 3 | 4 | 5 | 6 | 7 | 8 | 9 | 10 |
|----|----|----|----|----|----|----|----|----|-----|
| 11 | 12 | 13 | 14 | 15 | 16 | 17 | 18 | 19 | 20 |
| 21 | 22 | 23 | 24 | 25 | 26 | 27 | 28 | 29 | 30 |
| 31 | 32 | 33 | 34 | 35 | 36 | 37 | 38 | 39 | 40 |
| 41 | 42 | 43 | 44 | 45 | 46 | 47 | 48 | 49 | 50 |
| 51 | 52 | 53 | 54 | 55 | 56 | 57 | 58 | 59 | 60 |
| 61 | 62 | 63 | 64 | 65 | 66 | 67 | 68 | 69 | 70 |
| 71 | 72 | 73 | 74 | 75 | 76 | 77 | 78 | 79 | 80 |
| 81 | 82 | 83 | 84 | 85 | 86 | 87 | 88 | 89 | 90 |
| 91 | 92 | 93 | 94 | 95 | 96 | 97 | 98 | 99 | 100 |

• **There are 10 numbers that reduce to the number** [4] **in one or two steps. Colour them red.**

• **There are 10 numbers that reduce to the number** [9] **in one or two steps. Colour them green.**

**Teachers' note** In the oral/mental starter, practise adding digits in this way. This is sometimes known as finding the digital root. Encourage the children to look for and describe the patterns they see on the 100-square, for example, the patterns for numbers that reduce to 3, 5, 7, etc. Note that there are 11 ways, not 10, to reduce to the number 1. Use page 17 to extend this idea.

**Developing Numeracy**
**Solving Problems Year 6**
**© A & C Black**

You can reduce these numbers to a single-digit number by adding the digits. If the answer has more than one digit, keep adding the digits until you reach a single-digit number.

1123 → ⑦          8675 → 26 → ⑧

• **Which single-digit number do these reduce to?**

1473 → ___ → ◯          163 → ___ → ◯          10003 → ◯

2246 → ___ → ◯          146 → ___ → ◯          100101 → ◯

• **Find which numbers between 10 and 200 reduce to the number ⬚2⬚ .**

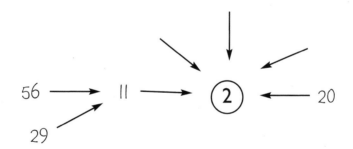

56 ——→ 11 ——→ ② ←—— 20

29 ——↗

• **Find which numbers between 10 and 300 reduce to the number ⬚3⬚ in one step.**
• **Then find numbers that reduce to the number ⬚3⬚ in two steps.**

**Teachers' note** In the oral/mental starter, practise adding digits in this way. This is sometimes known as finding the digital root. Page 16 can be used as an introduction. Encourage the children to be systematic in finding numbers that reduce to a number in two steps, for example, 39 or 48 reduce to 12, then reduce to 3. Emphasise that single-digit numbers cannot be reduced.

**Developing Numeracy
Solving Problems Year 6
© A & C Black**

# Flash digits

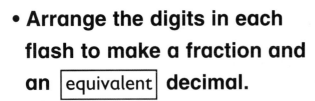

- **Arrange the digits in each flash to make a fraction and an** |equivalent| **decimal.**

Use a calculator to help you.

**1.**  5 0 1 2
$\frac{1}{2}$ = ⓪ · ⑤

**2.** 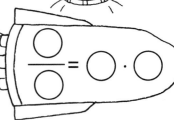 7 1 5 4
$\frac{\ }{\ }$ = ◯ · ◯◯

**3.**  5 5 2 2
$\frac{\ }{\ }$ = ◯ · ◯◯

**4.** 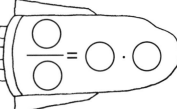 6 1 9 5
$\frac{\ }{\ }$ = ◯ · ◯◯

**5.**  6 5 2 1
$\frac{\ }{\ }$ = ◯ · ◯◯

**6.** 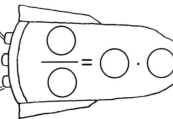 6 1 4 5
$\frac{\ }{\ }$ = ◯ · ◯◯

**7.**  6 5 3 0
$\frac{\ }{\ }$ = ◯ · ◯◯

**8.** 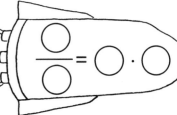 8 1 9 5
$\frac{\ }{\ }$ = ◯ · ◯◯

**9.**  5 7 3 2
$\frac{\ }{\ }$ = ◯ · ◯◯

**10.** 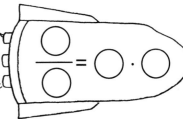 0 2 4 5
$\frac{\ }{\ }$ = ◯ · ◯◯

 Now try this!

- **Re-arrange these digits to make a fraction and an** |equivalent| **decimal.**

0   3   3
7   8   5

$\frac{\ }{\ }$ = ◯ · ◯◯◯

**Teachers' note** During the oral/mental starter, revise the word 'equivalent' and discuss how to use a calculator to convert a fraction to a decimal, for example, 2 ÷ 5 = 0·4. The children can create their own 'flash digits' using a calculator, for a partner to solve.

**Developing Numeracy
Solving Problems Year 6
© A & C Black**

18

# Dicey moments

• **Stand two dice on top of each other to make a tower.**

**1.** Arrange the dice so that there are the same
number of spots on each side of the tower.
Draw the spots on each side of the tower.

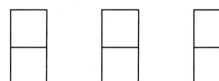

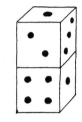

• **Stand four dice on top of each other to make a tower.**

**2.** Arrange the dice so that there are the same
number of spots on each side of the tower.
Draw the spots on each side of the tower.

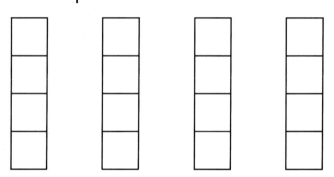

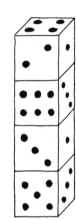

**3.** Arrange the dice so that there are ⬚three⬚ times as
many spots on one side as on the opposite side.
Draw the spots on each side of the tower.

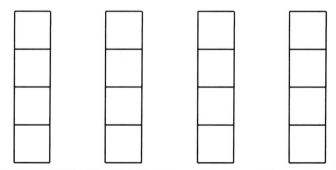

• **Is it possible to arrange** ⬚three⬚ **dice in a tower**
**with the same number of spots on each side?**

• **Is it possible with** ⬚five⬚ **dice?**

**Teachers' note** Encourage the children to think about these investigations rather than just using a trial and error strategy. Begin the lesson by talking about the totals on opposite faces of a dice and discussing the number of spots on one, two, three dice, etc. The children could use dice made from cubes with dots stuck on, if no real dice are available.

**Developing Numeracy**
**Solving Problems Year 6**
**© A & C Black**

# Zip Zap puzzles: 1

This grid shows six 3-digit numbers.

They are made from the digits 1 to 9.

Read 'Zap' numbers across.
Example: **Zap 1** is 219.

Read 'Zip' numbers down.
Example: **Zip 1** is 247.

| Zip 1↓ | Zip 2↓ | Zip 3↓ |
|:---:|:---:|:---:|
| 2 | 1 | 9 |
| 4 | 8 | 3 |
| 7 | 6 | 5 |

Zap 1 → 2 1 9
Zap 2 → 4 8 3
Zap 3 → 7 6 5

- **Read the clues.**
- **Write all the digits 1 to 9 on the grid.**

**1.** **ACROSS**
   **Zap 1** is a multiple of 5 and 83.
   **Zap 2** is greater than 800 and is a multiple of 8.
   **Zap 3** is an odd number. The sum of the first two
      digits equals the last digit.

   **DOWN**
   **Zip 1** is a multiple of 3 smaller than 500.
   **Zip 2** is the smallest number. It is a multiple
      of 8 and 22.
   **Zip 3** is an odd square number with 23 as a factor.

| 4 | 1 | 5 |
|:---:|:---:|:---:|
|  |  |  |
|  |  |  |

**2.** **ACROSS**
   **Zap 1** is an even number. It is 9 less than Zip 1.
   **Zap 2** is the largest number. It is a multiple of 5.
   **Zap 3** is a square number less than 200.

   **DOWN**
   **Zip 1** is an odd number between 300 and 400.
   **Zip 2** is exactly divisible by 7.
   **Zip 3** is a square number.

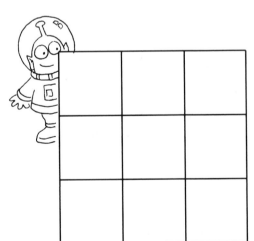

- **Make up your own Zip Zap grid.**
- **Write a clue for each number.**
- **Give it to a partner to solve.**

Use all the
digits 1 to 9.

**Teachers' note** Discuss that a zip goes up and down, for example on a coat, and that when a spaceship 'zaps' an alien it shoots across. This can help the children to remember which is which. The children should use trial and error to find which numbers fit both the Zip and Zap clues. The following activity is a further extension of the work on this page.

**Developing Numeracy**
**Solving Problems Year 6**
**© A & C Black**

# Zip Zap puzzles: 2

- **Read the clues.**
- **Complete the grids.**

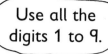

Use all the digits 1 to 9.

**1.** **ACROSS**

    **Zap 1** is an even number, exactly divisible by 8 and 109.

    **Zap 2** is exactly half of Zap 1.

    **Zap 3** is a multiple of 3. Its digits total 15.

    **DOWN**

    **Zip 1** is a square number over 800.

    **Zip 2** has the prime factors 3, 5 and 7.

    **Zip 3** is a prime number between 260 and 270.

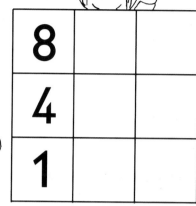

**2.** **ACROSS**

    **Zap 1** is a prime number between 100 and 130.

    **Zap 2** is divisible by 8.

    **Zap 3** has the prime factors 23 and 41.

    **DOWN**

    **Zip 1** has 9 and 7 as factors.

    **Zip 2** is exactly twice Zip 1.

    **Zip 3** is a multiple of 7.

**3.** **ACROSS**

    **Zap 1** is a multiple of 3 between 600 and 700. Its digits total 15.

    **Zap 2** is a multiple of 3. Its digits total 15.

    **Zap 3** has factors 3, 5, 7, 21, 35, 105, 147 and 245.

    **DOWN**

    **Zip 1** is exactly divisible by 3. Its digits total 15.

    **Zip 2** is the largest number. It is less than 899.

    **Zip 3** is the smallest number. It is a multiple of 15 and 13. Its digits total 15.

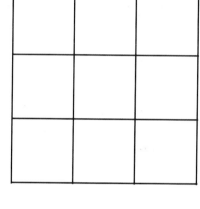

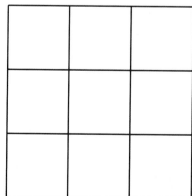

**Teachers' note** The children should first complete the activity 'Zip Zap puzzles: 1' on page 20. They will need calculators for this activity.

**Developing Numeracy Solving Problems Year 6 © A & C Black**

# Make your own ruler

**Here is an unmarked ruler.**

• **Follow the instructions to mark centimetres on the ruler.
You are not allowed to use your own ruler!**

**1.** Cut out the strips at the bottom of the sheet.

**2.** Using the strips, mark and label 7 cm and 10 cm from the left-hand end of the ruler.

**3.** Mark 17 cm.

Clue: use both strips.

**4.** Mark 3 cm, 14 cm and 4 cm.

Clue: use the strips and the marks already drawn.
10 − 7 = ?   7 + 7 = ?
14 − 10 = ?

**5.** Mark 13 cm, 6 cm and 16 cm.

Clue: 3 + 10 = ?
13 − 7 = ?

**6.** Mark 11 cm, 1 cm and 8 cm.

Clue: use addition and subtraction facts that you know.

**7.** Mark 18 cm, 15 cm and 5 cm.

**8.** Finally, mark 12 cm, 2 cm and 9 cm. Your ruler is complete!

|←——— 7 cm ———→|←——————— 10 cm ———————→|

**Teachers' note** As an extension, the children could make a ruler up to 30 cm, using strips measuring 8 cm and 11 cm.

**Developing Numeracy
Solving Problems Year 6
© A & C Black**

# Magic multiplication

For these questions you can add and subtract, but you are not allowed to multiply!

- **Look carefully at this fact.**

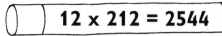

$$12 \times 212 = 2544$$

- **Use the fact to answer these questions.**

1.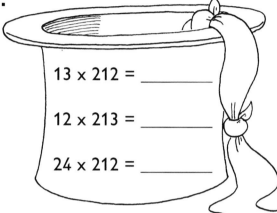

13 × 212 = _____

12 × 213 = _____

24 × 212 = _____

2.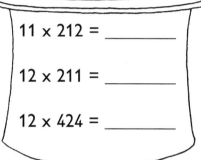

11 × 212 = _____

12 × 211 = _____

12 × 424 = _____

- **Look carefully at this fact.**

$$24 \times 114 = 2736$$

- **Use the fact to answer these questions.**

3.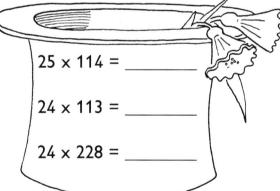

25 × 114 = _____

24 × 113 = _____

24 × 228 = _____

4.

23 × 114 = _____

24 × 115 = _____

48 × 114 = _____

**Now try this!**

- **Write as many multiplication statements as you can using this fact. Remember you are not allowed to multiply!**

$$16 \times 224 = 3584$$

**Teachers' note** The children can use the number statements they have derived from the fact to create new facts, for example, 14 × 212 can be found using the answer to 13 × 212.

**Developing Numeracy
Solving Problems Year 6
© A & C Black**

# Calculator clues

- **Copy a line from the box to complete each statement.**
- **Write at least three examples to prove it.**

Use a calculator to help you.

> I get a number that is four times smaller
> I get a number that is half as big
> I get a number that is 10 times smaller
> I get a number that is 10 times greater
> I get a number that is four times larger
> ✔ I get a number that is twice as big

**1.** If I divide a number by one half... _I get a number that is twice as big._

$10 \div 0.5 = 20$

$100 \div 0.5 = 200$

$4000 \div 0.5 = 8000$

**2.** If I multiply a number by 0·5...

**3.** If I multiply a number by one tenth...

**4.** If I divide a number by 0·1...

**5.** If I divide a number by 0·25...

**6.** If I multiply a number by one quarter...

**Teachers' note** The children may need practice in converting fractions to decimals. Discuss with them the importance of finding more than one example to prove a general statement.

**Developing Numeracy
Solving Problems Year 6
© A & C Black**

# Calculator clues

- **Copy a line from the box to complete each statement.**
- **Write at least three examples to prove it.**

Use a calculator to help you.

> I get a number that is five times smaller
> I get a number that is nine times larger
> I get a number that is four times smaller
> ✔ I get a number that is eight times greater
> I get a number that is five times larger
> I get a number that is three times bigger

**1.** If I divide a number by 0·125... *I get a number that is eight times greater.*

$10 \div 0.125 = 80$

$100 \div 0.125 = 800$

$1000 \div 0.125 = 8000$

**2.** If I divide a number by 0·2...

**3.** If I multiply a number by one fifth...

**4.** If I divide a number by 0·1111111...

**5.** If I divide a number by 0·333333...

**6.** If I multiply a number by 2 and divide by 8...

---

**Teachers' note** The children may need practice in converting fractions to decimals. Discuss with them the importance of finding more than one example to prove a general statement. Some of these questions involve recurring decimals. Discuss rounding these decimals with the children.

**Developing Numeracy Solving Problems Year 6** © A & C Black

# Find the link

**These questions are all linked. They can be worked out in similar ways.**

How many weeks are there in 2 years?

How many weeks are there in 4 years?

How many weeks are there in 100 years?

**1.** Write a formula to show the number of weeks in *n* years.

number of weeks = _____

**These questions are all linked, too.**

Chews cost 4p each. How much will 6 chews cost?

Chews cost 4p each. How much will 11 chews cost?

Chews cost 4p each. How much will 7 chews cost?

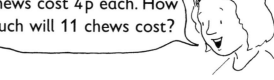

**2.** Write a formula to show the cost of *n* chews at 4p each.

cost = _____

**3.** Write a formula to show the cost of *n* CDs at £6 each.

cost = _____

**4.** Write a formula to show the number of days in *n* years.

_____

**5.** Write a formula to show the cost of *n* apples at 37p each.

_____

Now try this!

• **Write a formula to show the number of** | minutes |

**in *n*** | days |.

Teachers' note Before beginning this activity, discuss formulae and, if necessary, provide further
practice in describing relationships like these in words before the children attempt to write a
formula. In question 1, the children should approximate to 52 weeks in a year. During the plenary,
discuss whether any children considered leap years for question 4.

Developing Numeracy
Solving Problems Year 6
© A & C Black

# Hands off!

• **Fill in this chart.**

| Number of hands | 1 | 2 | 3 | 4 | 5 | 6 | 7 | 8 | 9 | 10 | 100 |
|---|---|---|---|---|---|---|---|---|---|---|---|
| Number of thumbs | 1 | | | | | | | | | | |
| Number of fingers | 4 | | | | | | | | | | |
| Number of nails | 5 | | | | | | | | | | |

**1.** Write a formula to show the number of

fingers on *n* hands _____

thumbs on *n* hands _____

nails on *n* hands _____

• **Fill in this chart.**

| Number of people | 1 | 2 | 3 | 4 | 5 | 6 | 7 | 8 | 9 | 10 | 100 |
|---|---|---|---|---|---|---|---|---|---|---|---|
| Number of feet | | | | | | | | | | | |
| Number of toes | | | | | | | | | | | |
| Number of toenails | | | | | | | | | | | |

**2.** Write a formula to show the number of

feet that *n* people have _____

toes that *n* people have _____

toenails that *n* people have _____

Now try this!

• **Draw an alien. Write your own formulae for how many body parts it has.**

**Teachers' note** This activity encourages children to realise the importance of finding a general formula that works for all numbers. Once a formula has been written, encourage the children to substitute real numbers, for example, 1000, 500 and so on, in place of *n* in the formula.

**Developing Numeracy
Solving Problems Year 6
© A & C Black**

# What's inside?

- **Solve these puzzles.**

**1.** In this room there are some people and some fish.
There are 20 eyes and 14 legs.
How many people? _____
How many fish? _____

**2.** In this room there are some people and some dogs.
There are 14 eyes and 18 legs.
How many people? _____
How many dogs? _____

**3.** In this room there are some dogs and some fish.
There are 10 eyes and 16 legs.
How many dogs? _____
How many fish? _____

**4.** In this room there are some people and some spiders.
There are 20 eyes and 50 legs.
How many people? _____
How many spiders? _____

**5.** In this room there are some people and some cats.
There are 16 eyes and 8 hands.
How many people? _____
How many cats? _____

**6.** In this room there are some people and some dogs.
There are 14 noses and 8 tails.
How many people? _____
How many dogs? _____

**In my house there are some fish, people and dogs.**
**There are** 28 legs , 24 eyes , 12 mouths **and** 8 tails .

- **How many**

fish? _____          people? _____          dogs? _____

**Teachers' note** Discuss the number of eyes, noses, mouths, tails, etc. that the animals on this page have. It is assumed that fish, dogs and cats have a tail each, that all animals and people have two eyes, a mouth, and so on. Encourage the children to solve these problems algebraically.

**Developing Numeracy**
**Solving Problems Year 6**
**© A & C Black**

28

# An *x*-citing formula!

**• Join each situation to its formula.**

**1.** Clare has 8 pence in her purse. She is given *x* pence. How much does she have now?

$x \div 2$

**2.** Mike scores *x* goals. Jake scores half as many. How many goals does Jake score?

$8 + x$

**3.** A CD which cost £8 is reduced by £*x* in the sale. How much does the CD cost now?

$x - 2$

**4.** Tim is given £*x* for his birthday. He spends £8. How much has he got left?

$8 - x$

**5.** Mrs Jones bakes *x* cakes. She gives two of them away. How many does she keep?

$x + 2$

**6.** Alia has *x* rides on the dodgems. Kim has twice as many. How many rides does Kim have?

$x - 8$

**7.** Jackie spends £*x* in the grocer's and £2 in the sweet shop. How much does she spend?

$2x$

**Now try this!**

**• Write a formula for this situation.**

There are *x* people on a bus. When it stops, *y* people get off and *z* people get on. _____

**Teachers' note** The children will need some experience of devising formulae of this kind (see pages 26 and 27). Ensure that the children appreciate that *x* can stand for any number in these situations.

**Developing Numeracy**
**Solving Problems Year 6**
© A & C Black

29

# Shape shuffle

• **Name these** quadrilaterals .

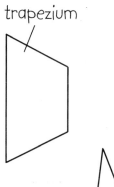
trapezium

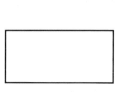

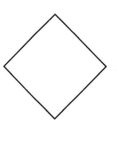

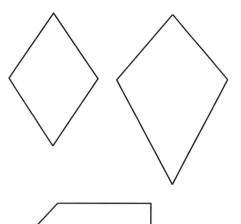

## The shapes below are made from two quadrilaterals.

• **Draw lines to show the join. The quadrilaterals can be different shapes and sizes from the ones above.**

trapezium and parallelogram

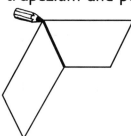

square and kite

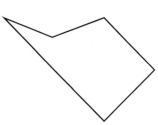

kite and kite

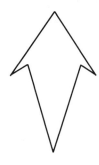

trapezium and rhombus

rectangle and kite

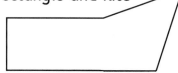

rhombus and rhombus

kite and parallelogram

trapezium and trapezium

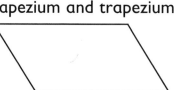

Now try this!

**This shape is made from two** quadrilaterals .

• **Draw lines to show the join.**

• **Name the two quadrilaterals.**

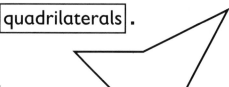

---

**Teachers' note** Discuss the properties of quadrilaterals and ensure that the children know the definitions of the different types. If necessary, explain that a kite which is not convex is also known as an 'arrowhead'. As a further extension activity, the children could draw their own shapes made from two quadrilaterals and give them to a partner to solve.

**Developing Numeracy Solving Problems Year 6 © A & C Black**

# Split it!

Farmer Giles wants to split his
rectangular field into two parts.
He has one straight line of fence.

**1.** Into what shapes could he split the field with one straight line?

I triangle and
I trapezium

**2.** Imagine Farmer Giles has two straight lines of fence. What shapes could he make now?

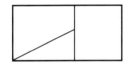      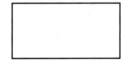

I trapezium,
I triangle, I rectangle

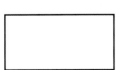      

**Teachers' note** Revise the names and properties of the different types of quadrilateral before the children begin this sheet. There are obviously an infinite number of ways of splitting a rectangle, but encourage the children to find as many different 'types' of shape combinations as they can, for example, triangle/triangle/triangle or triangle/triangle/quadrilateral.

**Developing Numeracy
Solving Problems Year 6
© A & C Black**

# Going dotty

- **Join the dots on the grid to make** [squares] **and** [rectangles].
- **Draw as many different ones as you can. Reflections, rotations and translations all count as the same shape.**

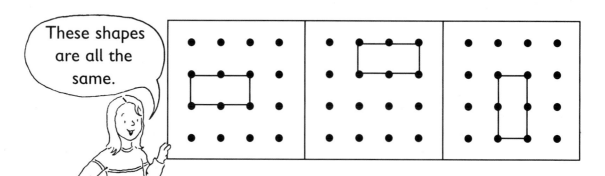

These shapes are all the same.

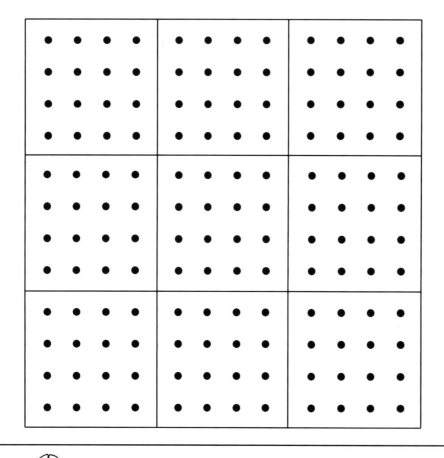

Try diagonal lines!

Now try this!

- **Number each shape and work out its area.**

1. _____ squares     2. _____ squares     3. _____ squares

4. _____ squares     5. _____ squares     6. _____ squares

7. _____ squares     8. _____ squares     9. _____ squares

**Teachers' note** Remind the children of the meaning of the words 'rotation', 'reflection' and 'translation', and ensure that they appreciate when two shapes are classed as the same for this activity. Provide copies of page 38 for children who require additional grids for the activity.

**Developing Numeracy
Solving Problems Year 6
© A & C Black**

# Going dotty

- **Join the dots on the grid to make** parallelograms **which do not have any right angles.**
- **Draw as many different ones as you can. Reflections, rotations and translations all count as the same shape.**

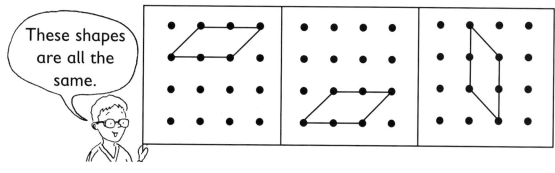

These shapes are all the same.

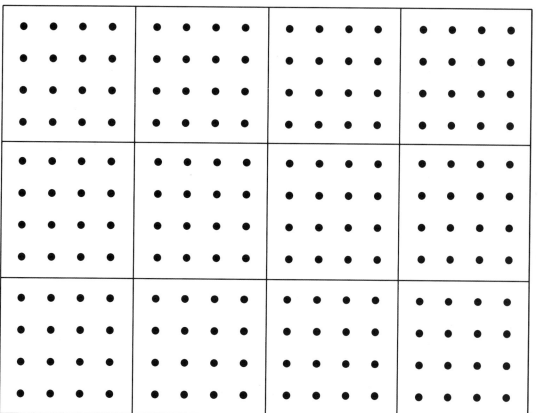

Now try this!

- **There is only one way of drawing a** rhombus **on this grid. Draw it here.**
- **What is special about a** rhombus **?**

_____

_____

**Teachers' note** Discuss the properties of parallelograms, i.e. that they are quadrilaterals with two sets of parallel sides. Ensure that the children appreciate when two shapes are classed as the same for this activity. Provide copies of page 38 for children who require additional grids for the activity. Further extension work can involve finding kites, trapeziums and other quadrilaterals.

**Developing Numeracy
Solving Problems Year 6
© A & C Black**

# It's just the half of it!

**Imagine this is half a shape.**   **This could be the whole shape**
**made from two identical halves.**

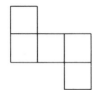   

**1.** Draw some more shapes which could be the whole shape.
   Mark on any lines of symmetry.

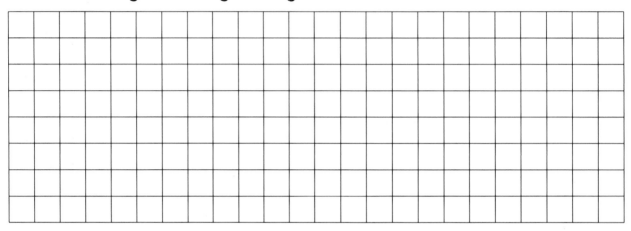

**Imagine this is half a shape.**   **This could be the whole shape**
**made from**
**two identical**
**halves.**

   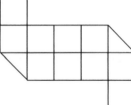

**2.** Draw some more shapes which could be the whole shape.
   Mark on any lines of symmetry.

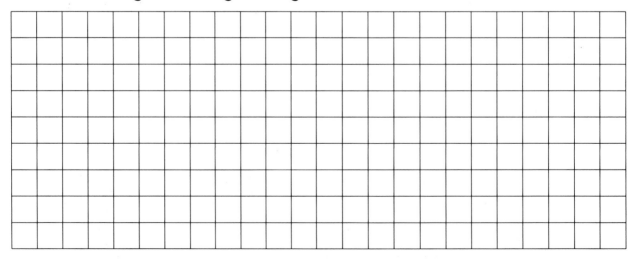

**Teachers' note** The children may find it easier to copy two of each shape onto squared paper and cut them out to rearrange. Remind the children that a half does not have to be the reflection of the other, for example, the whole shape could be made from the half shape and its translation or rotation.

**Developing Numeracy**
**Solving Problems Year 6**
**© A & C Black**

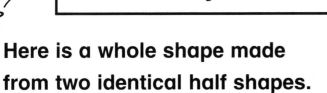
# It's just the half of it!

Here is a whole shape made
from two identical half shapes.

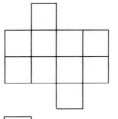

This could be the half shape.

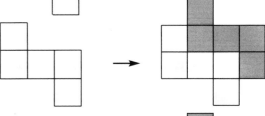

Or this could be the half shape.

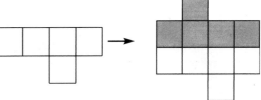

**1.** Draw another shape that
could be the half shape.

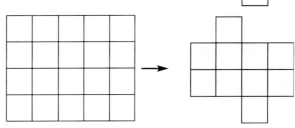

**2.** Here is a whole shape. Draw three different shapes that could be
the half shape.

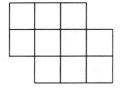 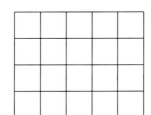 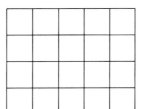 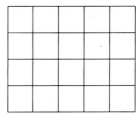

**3.** Here is a whole shape. Draw four different shapes that could be
the half shape.

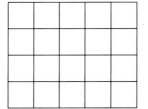 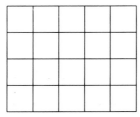 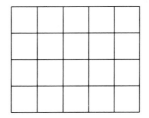

**Teachers' note** Remind the children that a half does not have to be a reflection of the other,
for example, the whole shape could be made from the half shape and its translation or rotation.
Shapes must be identical, not just shapes with the same area.

**Developing Numeracy
Solving Problems Year 6
© A & C Black**

# Try-angles!

Sanjay is measuring angles
with a protractor.

When I measure the three
angles in a triangle, they
always add up to 180°.

Here are the ⎡triangles⎤ Sanjay is measuring.

• **Measure the angles to see whether he is right.**

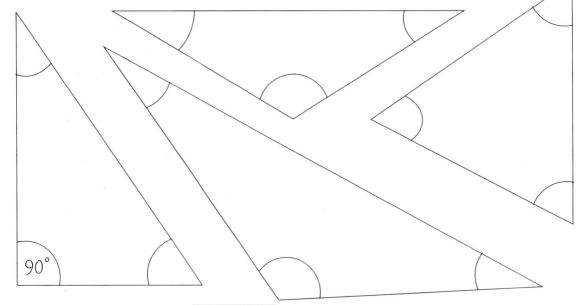

• **Draw some more** ⎡triangles⎤ **to test whether this always works.**

• **Do the angles in a** ⎡triangle⎤ **always add up to** ⎡180°⎤**?** _____

Teachers' note Discuss the different types of triangles, for example, right-angled scalene,
right-angled isosceles, scalene, isosceles and equilateral. Encourage the children to draw and
measure angles of all types to test the rule. Reassure the children that, because of inaccuracy
of measuring, the answer may not always be exactly 180°.

Developing Numeracy
Solving Problems Year 6
© A & C Black

# Pick's theorem

A man called Mr Pick noticed something about finding the area of a shape on a dotty grid.

• **Read what he says.**

1) I count the number of dots on the perimeter.
2) I divide this number by 2.
3) Then I add the number of dots inside the shape.
4) Finally, I take away 1.
The answer is always the same as the area of the shape.

1) Perimeter has 8 dots
2) $8 ÷ 2 = 4$
3) $4 + 1 = 5$
4) $5 - 1 = 4$
**area = 4 squares**

• **Draw shapes on the grids. Follow Mr Pick's instructions to test whether his idea always works.**

**Teachers' note** Provide copies of page 38 for children who require additional grids for this activity. Encourage the children to record carefully. Ask questions such as, 'Does this work for all rectangles? What about all triangles?' 'How do you find the area of other quadrilaterals?' To check their answers, the children may have to break up the shape into smaller shapes.

**Developing Numeracy
Solving Problems Year 6
© A & C Black**

37

# Dotty resource sheet

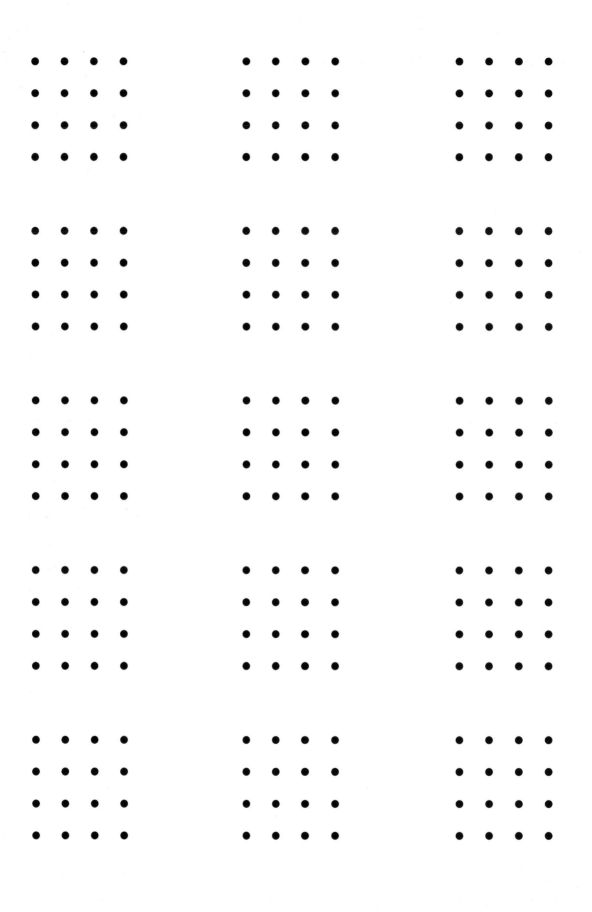

**Teachers' note** Provide copies of this sheet for children to record their answers for pages 32, 33 and 37.

**Developing Numeracy
Solving Problems Year 6
© A & C Black**

# Writer's block

An author is writing a 48-page book.

• **Complete the chart to show how long it takes.**

| Day | Number of pages written today | Total number of pages written so far | Fraction of book written so far |
|---|---|---|---|
| Monday | 1 | 1 | $\frac{1}{48}$ |
| Tuesday | 1 | 2 | |
| Wednesday | 1 | 3 | $\frac{1}{16}$ |
| Thursday | 1 | 4 | |
| Friday | 2 | | $\frac{1}{8}$ |
| Saturday | 2 | 8 | |
| Sunday | 4 | 12 | $\frac{1}{4}$ |
| Monday | 4 | | |
| Tuesday | 8 | 24 | |
| Wednesday | 12 | | $\frac{3}{4}$ |
| Thursday | 12 | 48 | 1 |

• **Another author is writing a 36-page book. Fill in the chart.**

| Day | Number of pages written today | Total number of pages written so far | Fraction of book written so far |
|---|---|---|---|
| Monday | 2 | 2 | $\frac{1}{18}$ |
| Tuesday | 1 | | |
| Wednesday | 1 | | |
| Thursday | 2 | | |
| Friday | 3 | | |
| Saturday | 9 | | |
| Sunday | | 36 | 1 |

An author has to write a 24-page book in five days.

• **Draw a chart to show how she could do this.**

Teachers' note Revise fractions during the oral/mental starter. The numbers in the chart can be masked before photocopying, and others inserted, to create a flexible resource.

Developing Numeracy
Solving Problems Year 6
© A & C Black

# Olympic dates

The Olympic games have taken place every [four] years, apart from during World War I and World War II.

| Year | City | Country |
|------|------|---------|
| 1896 | Athens | Greece |
| 1900 | Paris | France |
| 1904 | St Louis | USA |
| 1908 | London | UK |
| 1912 | Stockholm | Sweden |
| 1920 | Antwerp | Belgium |
| 1924 | Paris | France |
| 1928 | Amsterdam | Holland |
| 1932 | Los Angeles | USA |
| 1936 | Berlin | Germany |
| 1948 | London | UK |
| 1952 | Helsinki | Finland |

| Year | City | Country |
|------|------|---------|
| 1956 | Melbourne | Australia |
| 1960 | Rome | Italy |
| 1964 | Tokyo | Japan |
| 1968 | Mexico City | Mexico |
| 1972 | Munich | W. Germany |
| 1976 | Montreal | Canada |
| 1980 | Moscow | USSR |
| 1984 | Los Angeles | USA |
| 1988 | Seoul | S. Korea |
| 1992 | Barcelona | Spain |
| 1996 | Atlanta | USA |
| 2000 | Sydney | Australia |

**1.** How many times have the games been held in the USA? _____

**2.** How many years apart were the two Olympic games held in

London? _____    Paris? _____    Los Angeles? _____

**3.** How many years ago were the games held in

Helsinki? _____    Amsterdam? _____    Tokyo? _____

**4.** In which city were the games held

16 years after Athens? _____

28 years before Tokyo? _____

**5.** How many years ago were the games held in

Spain? _____    Mexico? _____    Belgium? _____

Now try this!

• **Three Olympic games were cancelled because of World Wars I and II. Write the dates.**

• **When will the next [10] Olympic games be held?**

**Teachers' note** Ensure that the children know that the years of the Olympic games are always multiples of four. Discuss the test of divisibility by four, i.e. that the number made by the last two digits of the number, when halved, is even. Some dates from the second chart could be masked before photocopying for the children to complete.

**Developing Numeracy Solving Problems Year 6 © A & C Black**

# Football crazy

Here is part of a football table. The first column (P) tells you how many matches each team has played. The other columns show how many matches were won (W), drawn (D) or lost (L).

3 points are scored for a win, 1 for a draw and 0 for a loss.

| | P | W | D | L | Points |
|---|---|---|---|---|---|
| **TOP OF TABLE** | | | | | |
| Man Utd | 32 | 21 | 9 | 2 | ___ |
| Chelsea | 32 | 20 | 7 | 5 | ___ |
| Newcastle | 32 | 17 | 6 | 9 | ___ |
| Arsenal | 32 | 15 | 12 | 5 | ___ |
| Leeds | 33 | 14 | 13 | 6 | ___ |
| Liverpool | 33 | 15 | 8 | 10 | ___ |
| Aston Villa | 33 | 13 | 10 | 10 | ___ |

1. Work out how many points each team has. Fill in the 'points' column.

**The next match was Man Utd v Arsenal. It was a** [draw].

• **First, update the table. Then answer these questions.**

**2.** How many points do Man Utd have? ___

**3.** How many points do Arsenal have? ___

**4.** How many games have Man Utd played? ___

**5.** What position in the table are Arsenal now? ___

**6.** How many more points than Chelsea do Man Utd have? ___

**7.** How many more points than Newcastle do Arsenal have? ___

Now try this!

**Here are the results of the next three matches.**

• **Write the new table, showing these results.**

Chelsea beat Leeds
Liverpool beat Newcastle
Aston Villa and Arsenal draw

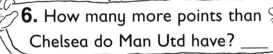

---

Teachers' note Some children may already be familiar with football tables and could be given a greater range of results to explore. Ensure that the children understand the column headings and the points system. You could use the 'Football tables' activity on page 5 to introduce this.

Developing Numeracy
Solving Problems Year 6
© A & C Black

# Car park chaos

- **Find your way out of the car park by answering the questions.**

Multi – Storey

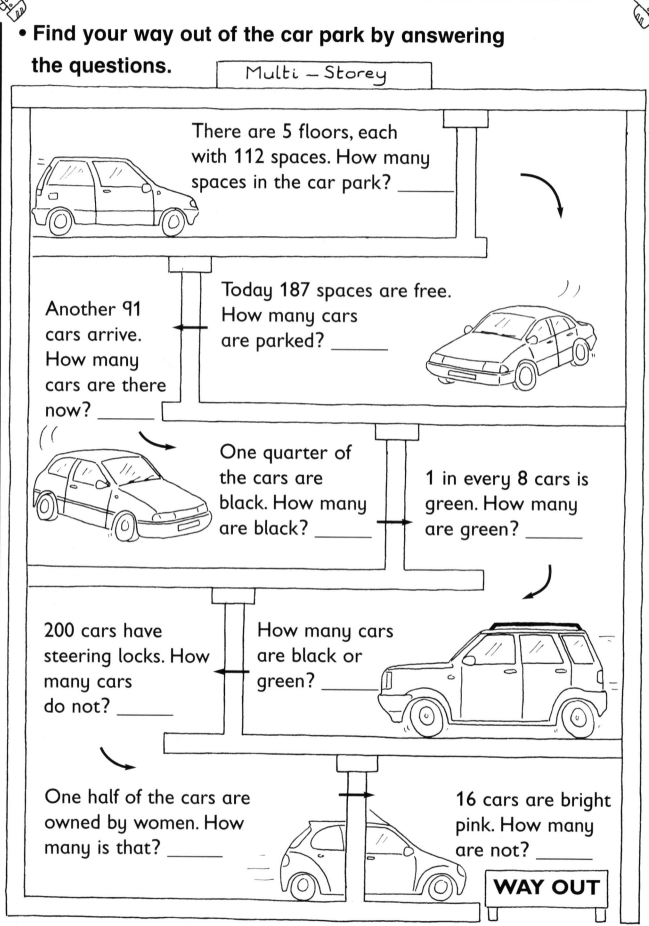

There are 5 floors, each with 112 spaces. How many spaces in the car park? _____

Today 187 spaces are free. How many cars are parked? _____

Another 91 cars arrive. How many cars are there now? _____

One quarter of the cars are black. How many are black? _____

1 in every 8 cars is green. How many are green? _____

200 cars have steering locks. How many cars do not? _____

How many cars are black or green? _____

One half of the cars are owned by women. How many is that? _____

16 cars are bright pink. How many are not? _____

**WAY OUT**

Teachers' note  Some of these questions involve ratio and proportion. The children could work in pairs to solve the questions. The following sheet provides more of a challenge and includes multi-step operations.

Developing Numeracy
Solving Problems Year 6
© A & C Black

# Car park chaos

- **Find your way out of the car park by answering the questions.**

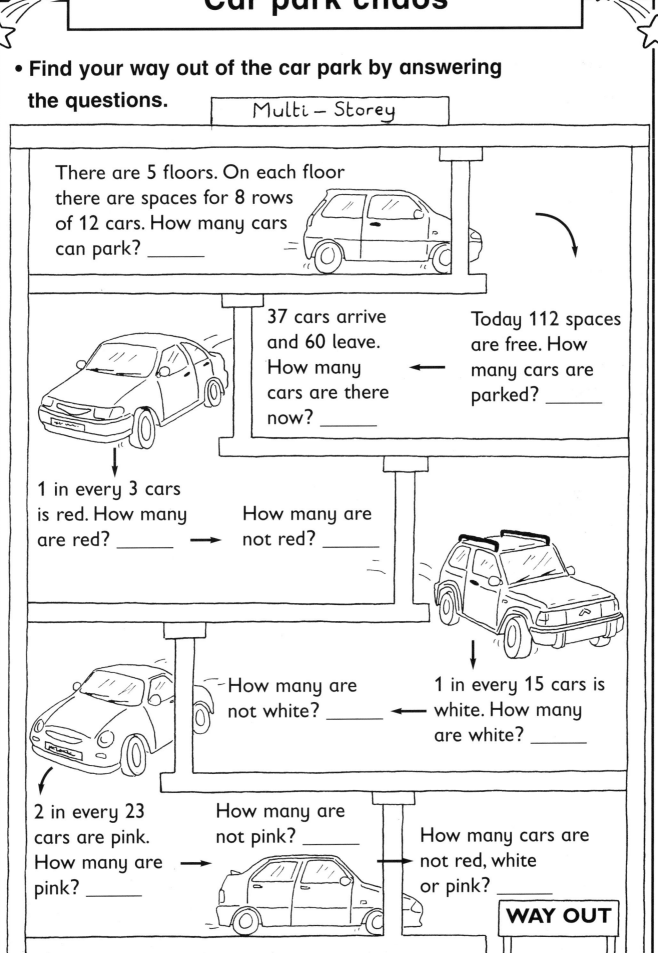

Multi – Storey

There are 5 floors. On each floor there are spaces for 8 rows of 12 cars. How many cars can park? _____

Today 112 spaces are free. How many cars are parked? _____

37 cars arrive and 60 leave. How many cars are there now? _____

1 in every 3 cars is red. How many are red? _____ → How many are not red? _____

How many are not white? _____ ← 1 in every 15 cars is white. How many are white? _____

2 in every 23 cars are pink. How many are pink? _____ → How many are not pink? _____

How many cars are not red, white or pink? _____

**WAY OUT**

**Teachers' note** Some of these questions involve ratio and proportion. The children could work in pairs to solve the questions. Most questions are multi-step. The previous page provides one-step operations.

**Developing Numeracy
Solving Problems Year 6
© A & C Black**

43

# Speed, camera, action!

**The police in Nickham have caught some cars speeding.**

**1.** How many miles per hour (mph) <u>over</u> the speed limit was each car travelling? Fill in the charts.

| Cars caught in the ⑷⓪ miles per hour speed limit | Speed the cars were travelling (mph) | Mph over the speed limit |
|---|---|---|
| Nissan Micra | 44 | 4 |
| Ford Escort | 41 | |
| BMW | 48 | |
| Austin Mini | 50 | |
| Porsche | 47 | |
| VW Golf | 52 | |

| Cars caught in the ⑹⓪ miles per hour speed limit | Speed the cars were travelling (mph) | Mph over the speed limit |
|---|---|---|
| Ford Ka | 68 | |
| VW Beetle | 72 | |
| Peugeot 106 | 80 | |
| Ford Sierra | 69 | |
| Honda Accord | 70 | |
| Renault Clio | 65 | |
| Toyota Corolla | 63 | |

**2.** What is the difference in speeds between these pairs of cars?

Austin Mini   and   Nissan Micra   _____ mph

Peugeot 106   and   Honda Accord   _____ mph

**Drivers who are caught speeding have to pay a fine.**

| | |
|---|---|
| Between 1 and 5 mph over the limit | £100 fine |
| Between 6 and 10 mph over the limit | £200 fine |
| More than 10 mph over the limit | £500 fine |

**3.** How much was the driver of the Ford Sierra fined? _____

**4.** How many drivers were fined  £100? _____   £200? _____   £500? _____

Now try this!

• **How much money was collected in fines?** _____

**Teachers' note** As a further extension, ask the children to work out how many kilometres per hour some of the cars were travelling, using the conversion 1 mile = 1·5 km.

**Developing Numeracy
Solving Problems Year 6
© A & C Black**

# Just chat!

- **Read these mobile phone adverts.**

> ### *Cheap Talk*
> Only 24p per minute
> at any time.
> **First minute free!**

> ☆ Talk for Less ☆
> 99p for each call under 10 minutes.
> 30p for each minute after that.

> ## Fast Chat
> 21p per minute at
> any time.

>
> ## Quick Call
> *11p per minute
> cheap rate.*
> *30p per minute between
> 9 am and 6 pm*

- **Work out how much each call would cost. Fill in the chart.**

| | | Cheap Talk | Talk for Less | Fast Chat | Quick Call |
|---|---|---|---|---|---|
| 1. | A 5-minute call at 9 o'clock in the evening. | 96p | | | |
| 2. | A 7-minute call at 7 o'clock in the morning. | | | | |
| 3. | An 8-minute call at 11 o'clock in the morning. | | | | |
| 4. | A 12-minute call at 2 o'clock in the afternoon. | | | | |
| 5. | A 15-minute call at 7 o'clock in the evening. | | | | |

**Teachers' note** Once the children have answered these questions, ask them to give each phone company a score for each situation, for example, Quick Call might score four points for being the cheapest in the first situation, Cheap Talk three points, Talk for Less two points and Fast Chat one point. The phone deals can then be compared across all situations.

**Developing Numeracy
Solving Problems Year 6
© A & C Black**

# Cheap flights

• **Read these flight adverts carefully.**

## Lo Fare

| | |
|---|---|
| Amsterdam | £50 |
| Zurich | £52 |
| Brussels | £60 |
| Glasgow | £58 |
| Athens | £75 |
| Ibiza | £60 |

## Cost Less

**Amsterdam, Zurich, Brussels, Glasgow, Athens, Ibiza**

*All flights £59*

## Fly Cheap!

**£10 off**
all prices below

| | | |
|---|---|---|
| Amsterdam | £62 | £52 |
| Zurich | £60 | |
| Brussels | £70 | |
| Glasgow | £67 | |
| Athens | £90 | |
| Ibiza | £72 | |

## BUDGET BUY!

**£20** extra charge on all prices below

| | |
|---|---|
| Amsterdam | £60 |
| Zurich | £32 |
| Brussels | £45 |
| Glasgow | £46 |
| Athens | £42 |
| Ibiza | £35 |

• **Which airline offers the cheapest flight to:**

Show your workings.

**1.** Amsterdam? _____

**2.** Zurich? _____

**3.** Brussels? _____

**4.** Glasgow? _____

**5.** Athens? _____

**6.** Ibiza? _____

**Teachers' note** Encourage the children to work in pairs or groups to find the prices of all the flights. As an extension, the prices can be recorded on a chart and presented to the rest of the class. The following sheet can be used to provide further extension work or to allow for differentiation in the lesson.

**Developing Numeracy**
**Solving Problems Year 6**
© A & C Black

• **Read these flight adverts carefully.**

## FARE DEALS

| | |
|---|---|
| Dublin | £75 |
| Los Angeles | £145 |
| New York | £162 |
| Barcelona | £89 |
| Paris | £66 |
| Madrid | £94 |

Plus **£25** airport tax on all flights.

## Lo Cost

**Dublin, Barcelona, Paris, Madrid**

*All flights* **£100**

*(no flights to New York or Los Angeles)*

## Flight Savers!

**10% off**
all prices below

| | | |
|---|---|---|
| Dublin | ~~£100~~ | £90 |
| Los Angeles | £200 | |
| New York | £190 | |
| Barcelona | £110 | |
| Paris | £110 | |
| Madrid | £120 | |

## Best Buy!

**£20** discount off all prices below

| | |
|---|---|
| Los Angeles | £200 |
| New York | £180 |
| Barcelona | £120 |
| Paris | £120 |

No flights to Dublin or Madrid.

• **Which airline offers the cheapest flight to:**

Show your workings.

1. Dublin? _____

2. Los Angeles? _____

3. New York? _____

4. Barcelona? _____

5. Paris? _____

6. Madrid? _____

**Teachers' note** Encourage the children to work in pairs or groups to find the prices of all the flights. As an extension, the prices can be recorded on a chart and presented to the rest of the class.

**Developing Numeracy
Solving Problems Year 6
© A & C Black**

# Star salaries

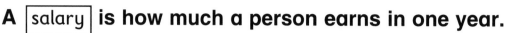

A $\boxed{\text{salary}}$ is how much a person earns in one year.

• Work out the $\boxed{\text{salary}}$ of each superstar.

**1.**

£ 408 000

TAKE TWO !

Greg Westward earns
£34 000 per month.

**2.**

HOLLYWOOD

Michelle Roberts earns
£8 000 per week.

**3.**

Kim Sprice earns
£1 000 per day.

**4.**

Bobbie Williamson earns
£50 per hour.

**5.**

Kathryn Ross earns
£1 per minute.

**6.**

Paul Kickham earns
1p per second.

Now try this!

• **About how many years would it take Paul Kickham to become a millionaire?** _____

**Teachers' note** Remind the children to watch out for changes of unit; they should notice that the last celebrity earns pence, not pounds. Explain to the children that the activity is not realistic as it assumes, for example, that Kathryn Ross works every minute of the day, every day of the year!

**Developing Numeracy
Solving Problems Year 6
© A & C Black**

# Great rates

This table shows exchange rates.

| £1 = | | |
|---|---|---|
| | 1.4 | Euros |
| | 1.8 | US Dollars |
| | 52.8 | Russian Rubles |
| | 200 | Japanese Yen |
| | 8910 | Zambia Kwacha |
| | 29750 | Vietnam Dong |

## These items cost the same in all the countries.

**1.** How much does this CD cost in:

HITS 40

£5

**USA?**  9 US dollars _____

**Japan?** _____

**France?** _____

**Zambia?** _____

**Vietnam?** _____

**Russia?** _____

**2.** How much does this orange cost in:

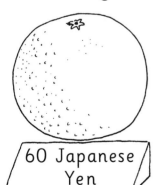

60 Japanese Yen

**UK?** _____

**Russia?** _____

**Spain?** _____

**USA?** _____

**Vietnam?** _____

**Zambia?** _____

Now try this!

• **How many** Vietnam Dong **would you get in exchange for one** Euro **?** _____

---

**Teachers' note** Encourage the children to estimate before using a calculator to find the answer. Remind them that when converting from pounds to other currencies, they should multiply by the exchange rate. When converting back to pounds, they should divide. Explain to the children that exchange rates vary. As a further extension, ask them to find the current exchange rates.

**Developing Numeracy
Solving Problems Year 6
© A & C Black 2000**

# Alligator swamp

• Colour the questions that have the answer $\boxed{9}$ to find a path through the swamp.

start

12% of 75  $\frac{1}{3}$ of 27  75% of 12

$\frac{7}{8}$ of 16  30% of 30  $\frac{1}{3}$ of 99  10% of 400

$\frac{3}{7}$ of 21  25% of 26  70% of 40  8% of 4

10% of 200

25% of 36  150% of 6  60% of 15

$\frac{4}{5}$ of 55  1% of 900  $\frac{1}{8}$ of 64  45% of 20

$\frac{1}{2}$ of 18  10% of 90  $\frac{1}{9}$ of 81

$\frac{1}{4}$ of 24  $\frac{7}{8}$ of 56

30% of 36

$\frac{1}{6}$ of 54

$\frac{1}{12}$ of 108  $\frac{3}{5}$ of 15

90% of 10  60% of 8

$\frac{1}{8}$ of 63  $\frac{5}{8}$ of 32  $\frac{4}{8}$ of 24

$\frac{1}{7}$ of 63  100% of 9

20% of 45  $\frac{3}{8}$ of 24

$\frac{45}{100}$ of 20

finish

**Teachers' note** The children could use this sheet with a calculator to practise finding percentages and fractions of numbers. These can be described in real situations involving money, for example, 'What is 12% of £75?'

**Developing Numeracy
Solving Problems Year 6
© A & C Black**

# Pitch it right

This chart shows the length and width of different sports pitches and courts. Each one is rectangular.

**1.** Find the area of each pitch or court. Complete the chart.

| | Length | Width | Area |
|---|---|---|---|
| Rugby | 100 m | 69 m | 6900 m² |
| Football | 120 m | 91 m | |
| Basketball | 26 m | 14 m | |
| American football | 110 m | 49 m | |
| Hockey | 91·4 m | 54·9 m | |
| Ice hockey | 61 m | 30·5 m | |
| Tennis (singles) | 23·77 m | 8·23 m | |
| Netball | 30·5 m | 15·2 m | |

**2.** Which has the largest area? _____

**3.** Which has the smallest area? _____

**4.** What is the difference in area between a rugby pitch and a football pitch? _____

**5.** What is the difference in area between a basketball court and a netball court? _____

**6.** What is the difference in area between a football pitch and an American football pitch? _____

**7.** Which pitches or courts have an area of less than 500 m²?

_____

**Teachers' note** Further questions of this type can be asked, based on the measurements in the chart. The children could use calculators if desired. Encourage the children to use m² as they write their answers. The children could measure the dimensions of the school's courts or pitches to see how these compare with the standard maximum recommended measurements.

Developing Numeracy
Solving Problems Year 6
© A & C Black

# Having a ball!

**This chart shows the measurements of balls used in different sports.**

| | Mass | Diameter | |
|---|---|---|---|
| Tennis ball | 58·9 g (2·063 oz) | 66·7 mm | (2·625 inches) |
| Squash ball | 24·6 g (0·87 oz) | 41·5 mm | (1·63 inches) |
| Football | 482 g (17 oz) | 300 mm | (11·8 inches) |
| Cricket ball | 163 g (5·75 oz) | 73·2 mm | (2·88 inches) |
| Table tennis ball | 2·53 g (0·089 oz) | 38 mm | (1·5 inches) |

**1.** List the balls in order of mass. Start with the lightest.

_____

_____

**2.** List the balls in order of size. Start with the smallest.

_____

_____

**3.** How many grams heavier is a tennis ball than a table tennis ball? _____

**4.** How many grams lighter is a cricket ball than a football? _____

**5.** How many ounces heavier is a cricket ball than a squash ball? _____

**6.** How many ounces lighter is a table tennis ball than a football? _____

**7.** How many millimetres more is the diameter of a cricket ball than a squash ball? _____

**8.** How many inches more is the diameter of a squash ball than a table tennis ball? _____

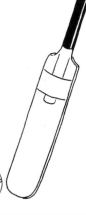

**Now try this!**

**A ball weighs** [72·4 g] **and has a diameter of** [82 mm].

• **Write the approximate measurements in** [ounces] **and** [inches]. **Use a calculator to help you.**

**Teachers' note** Further questions of this type can be asked, based on the measurements in the chart. The children could measure school balls and compare masses and diameters. They could also find the circumferences of these balls using pi.

**Developing Numeracy
Solving Problems Year 6
© A & C Black**

# Eating machine

This chart shows the number of **grams** of food that Shane ate during one week.

**1.** Fill in the total number of grams for each day.

| | Breakfast | Lunch | Evening meal | Total |
|---|---|---|---|---|
| Monday | 320 g | 527 g | 578 g | 1425 g |
| Tuesday | 310 g | 550 g | 502 g | |
| Wednesday | 322 g | 490 g | 600 g | |
| Thursday | 330 g | 515 g | 595 g | |
| Friday | 312 g | 480 g | 605 g | |
| Saturday | 500 g | 345 g | 515 g | |
| Sunday | 370 g | 460 g | 480 g | |

**2.** How many grams did Shane eat in the whole week? _____

**3.** Estimate how many grams Shane might eat in four weeks. _____

Use the number of grams I eat in one week.

**4.** Estimate how many grams Shane might eat in one year. Round the number to the nearest 100. _____

**5.** What is the average (mean) number of grams Shane eats for

breakfast? _____

lunch? _____

evening meal? _____

**Now try this!**

• **Estimate how many grams of food a person might eat in a lifetime. Use the rounded number in question 4.**

**Teachers' note** Encourage the children to give thought to the difference in amounts of food eaten by children and adults. An adult might eat twice as much as Shane. How many years are you a child? How many years an adult? What is an average lifetime? The children could use calculators if desired.

**Developing Numeracy
Solving Problems Year 6
© A & C Black**

# Quiz time

• **Colour the correct answer.**

**1.**

How many grams of carrots must I add to 2·69 kg to make 4 kg of carrots altogether?

| 2·69 g | 1310 g | 2690 g |

**2.**

What is the difference between 429 g of potatoes and $\frac{1}{2}$ kg of potatoes?

| 181 g | 571 g | 71 g |

**3.**

There are 2·2 kg of sugar in a bag. How many grams are in 5 bags?

| 11 000 g | 11 g | 110 g |

**4.**

1 ounce is approximately how many grams?

| 30 g | 50 g | 1000 g |

**5.**

1 kilogram is approximately how many pounds?

| 14 lb | 2·2 lb | 16 lb |

**6.**

A recipe uses 3 ounces of flour. Approximately how many grams is this?

| 36 g | 90 g | 150 g |

**7.**

How many grams of chocolate must I add to 6·32 kg to make 10 kg altogether?

| 3·68 g | 368 g | 3 680 g |

Now try this!

• **Approximately how many** ⎹ kilograms ⎸ **is** ⎹ 400 ounces ⎸?

---

**Teachers' note** Discuss the relationships between metric and imperial units of mass at the beginning of the lesson.

**Developing Numeracy**
**Solving Problems Year 6**
**© A & C Black**

54

# Recipe for success

• **Change these recipes to** $\boxed{\text{metric}}$ **units.**

**1.**

*Chocolate cupcakes*

| | |  | | |
|---|---|---|---|---|
| 2 oz | butter | | _____ 60 g _____ | butter |
| 5 oz | flour | | _____ | flour |
| 9 oz | chocolate | | _____ | chocolate |
| ½ lb | sugar | | _____ | sugar |
| Half a pint | milk | | _____ | milk |

**2.**

*Pastry*

| | | | | |
|---|---|---|---|---|
| ½ lb | lard | | _____ | lard |
| 2 lb | flour | | _____ | flour |
| 7 oz | margarine | | _____ | margarine |
| ¼ lb | sugar | | _____ | sugar |
| Half a pint | water | | _____ | water |

**3.**

*Vegetable soup*

| | | | | |
|---|---|---|---|---|
| 1 lb | carrots | | _____ | carrots |
| 7 oz | tomatoes | | _____ | tomatoes |
| ½ lb | onions | | _____ | onions |
| 2 lb | potatoes | | _____ | potatoes |
| Two pints | stock | | _____ | stock |

Now try this!

• **Find out how many millilitres of water a** $\boxed{\text{teaspoon}}$ **and a** $\boxed{\text{tablespoon}}$ **hold.**

• **How many** $\boxed{\text{teaspoons}}$ **of water would fill a pint jug?**

• **How many** $\boxed{\text{tablespoons}}$ **of water would fill a pint jug?**

**Teachers' note** Discuss the relationships between metric and imperial units of mass and capacity at the beginning of the lesson. To find the capacity of a teaspoon or a tablespoon in the extension activity, the children could first measure the capacity of 10, then divide to find an average. The children will need a measuring jug.

**Developing Numeracy
Solving Problems Year 6
© A & C Black**

# That sinking feeling!

• **Cut out the cards. Put each answer next to the correct question to make a loop.**

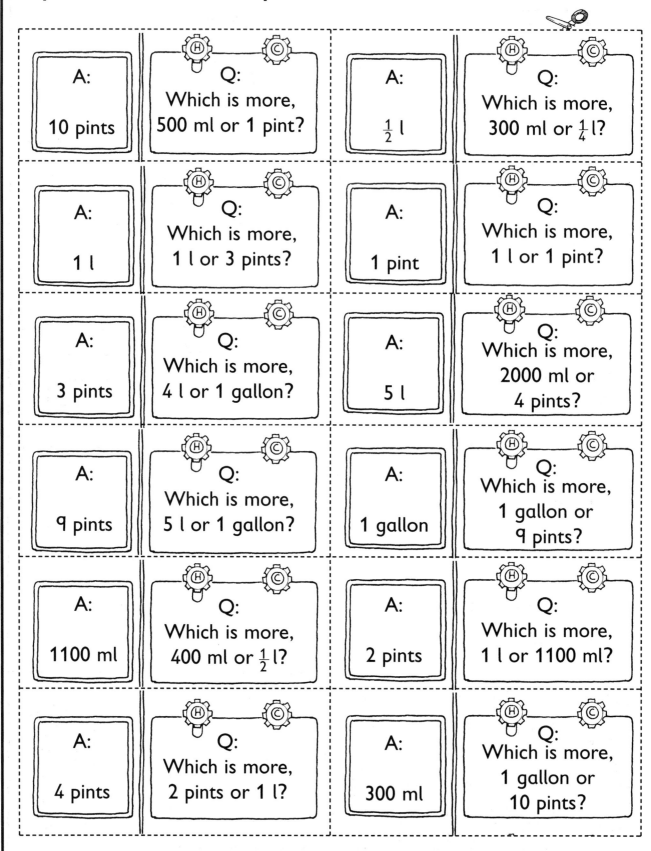

| A: 10 pints | Q: Which is more, 500 ml or 1 pint? | A: $\frac{1}{2}$ l | Q: Which is more, 300 ml or $\frac{1}{4}$ l? |
| A: 1 l | Q: Which is more, 1 l or 3 pints? | A: 1 pint | Q: Which is more, 1 l or 1 pint? |
| A: 3 pints | Q: Which is more, 4 l or 1 gallon? | A: 5 l | Q: Which is more, 2000 ml or 4 pints? |
| A: 9 pints | Q: Which is more, 5 l or 1 gallon? | A: 1 gallon | Q: Which is more, 1 gallon or 9 pints? |
| A: 1100 ml | Q: Which is more, 400 ml or $\frac{1}{2}$ l? | A: 2 pints | Q: Which is more, 1 l or 1100 ml? |
| A: 4 pints | Q: Which is more, 2 pints or 1 l? | A: 300 ml | Q: Which is more, 1 gallon or 10 pints? |

**Teachers' note** The cards form one continual loop. They can be used for a whole class or group activity, where each child has a card and the questions are read aloud. Provide the children with a list of the relationships between imperial and metric units of capacity.

**Developing Numeracy
Solving Problems Year 6
© A & C Black**

# Sunshine cocktail

**Alice is making sunshine cocktail for a party.**

**• Read the recipe.**

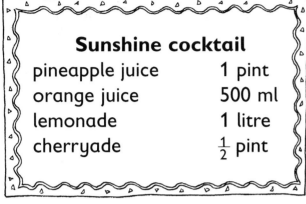

**Sunshine cocktail**

| | |
|---|---|
| pineapple juice | 1 pint |
| orange juice | 500 ml |
| lemonade | 1 litre |
| cherryade | $\frac{1}{2}$ pint |

**1.** Change the recipe to:

**millilitres**

pineapple juice _____ ml

orange juice _____ ml

lemonade _____ ml

cherryade _____ ml

**litres**

pineapple juice _____ l

orange juice _____ l

lemonade _____ l

cherryade _____ l

**2.** What is the total amount of cocktail Alice makes

in millilitres? _____     in litres? _____

**3.** About how many pints of cocktail does she make? _____

**4.** If Alice made twice as much cocktail, would this be more or less

than a gallon? _____

Now try this!

**• Tick the statements which are true.**

| | |
|---|---|
| A gallon is a bit less than 5 litres. | |
| A pint is slightly less than half a litre. | |
| There are 100 ml in a litre. | |
| 2 pints are just a bit more than 1 litre. | |
| 2 litres are a bit more than 1 pint. | |

**Teachers' note** During the first part of the lesson, discuss the children's favourite drinks, and combination 'cocktails' of these. Remind the children of the relationships between metric and imperial units of capacity.

**Developing Numeracy
Solving Problems Year 6
© A & C Black**

# Telly addict

• **Answer these video questions.**

**1.** I recorded a film during these times:
start 14:45      stop 17:25
For how long did the video record?

_2 hours 40 minutes_

**2.** I used a 3-hour video tape. How much recording time is left?

_____

**3.** Long play uses half as much tape as normal play. If I had used long play, how much recording time would be left?

_____

**4.** I watch a cartoon called Aliens from Pluto every day. It starts at 14:55 and finishes at 15:30. How long is the cartoon?

_____

**5.** How many hours and minutes of the cartoon do I watch in 7 days?

_____

**6.** How many episodes of the cartoon can I record on a 3-hour tape, if I use:

normal play?      long play?

_____

Now try this!

• **Write down three of your favourite programmes and their lengths.**
• **What is the total length of the programmes?**
• **If you recorded all of them on a 3-hour tape, how much time would be left?**

**Teachers' note** The children will need a television schedule for the extension activity. Revise the number of minutes in an hour and explain the meaning of 'long play' (it takes the same amount of time to record, but uses up half the space on the tape). Encourage the children to explain each situation to a partner.

**Developing Numeracy
Solving Problems Year 6
© A & C Black**

# Telly addict

• **Answer these video questions.**

**1.** I recorded a film during these times:

start 14:34     stop 16:17

For how long did the video record?

I hour 43 minutes

**2.** I used a 3-hour video tape. How much recording time is left?

**3.** Long play uses half as much tape as normal play. If I had used long play, how much recording time would be left?

**4.** I watch a cartoon called Aliens from Venus every day. It starts at 14:52 and finishes at 15:29. How long is the cartoon?

**5.** How many hours and minutes of the cartoon do I watch in 7 days?

**6.** How many episodes of the cartoon can I record on a 3-hour tape, if I use:

normal play?     long play?

Now try this!

• **Write down three of your favourite programmes and their lengths.**

• **What is the total length of the programmes in** | minutes |**?**

• **How many** | seconds | **is this?**

**Teachers' note** The children will need a television schedule for the extension activity. Revise the number of minutes in an hour and seconds in a minute, and explain the meaning of 'long play' (it takes the same amount of time to record, but uses up half the space on the tape). Encourage the children to explain each situation to a partner.

**Developing Numeracy
Solving Problems Year 6
© A & C Black**

# Tide times

**This table shows the times of high tide and low tide each day.**
**The tide comes in and goes out** `twice` **in about 24 hours.**

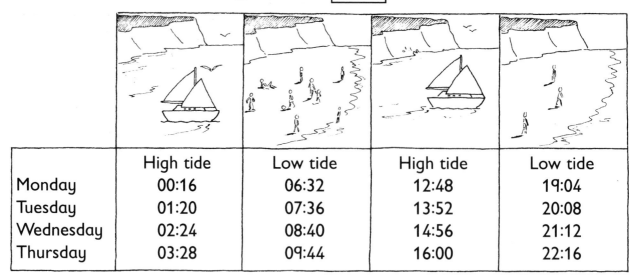

|  | High tide | Low tide | High tide | Low tide |
|---|---|---|---|---|
| Monday | 00:16 | 06:32 | 12:48 | 19:04 |
| Tuesday | 01:20 | 07:36 | 13:52 | 20:08 |
| Wednesday | 02:24 | 08:40 | 14:56 | 21:12 |
| Thursday | 03:28 | 09:44 | 16:00 | 22:16 |

**1.** What is the difference in time between the first high tide and the
first low tide:

on Monday?    <u>00:16 to 06:32</u>  = _____ hours and _____ minutes
on Tuesday?    _____ = _____ hours and _____ minutes
on Wednesday?    _____ = _____ hours and _____ minutes

What do you notice? _____

**2.** What is the difference in time between the first low tide and the
second high tide on each day? _____

**3.** What is the difference in time between the second high tide and
the second low tide on each day? _____

**4.** On Friday, the second low tide is at 23:20. Fill in the other
tide times for Friday.

| Friday |  |  |  | 23:20 |
|---|---|---|---|---|

• **Write all the tide times for Saturday and Sunday.**

**Teachers' note** Encourage the children to write down the times they are finding the difference
between and to show their workings. The following sheet can be used to provide further
extension on this theme. You could use the 'Time zones' activity on page 5 for practising
finding times.

**Developing Numeracy**
**Solving Problems Year 6**
**© A & C Black**

# Tide times

This table shows the times of high tide and low tide each day.
The tide comes in and goes out **twice** in about 24 hours.

|  | High tide | Low tide | High tide | Low tide |
|---|---|---|---|---|
| Monday | 00:13 | 06:29 | 12:45 | 19:01 |
| Tuesday | 01:17 | 07:33 | 13:49 | 20:05 |
| Wednesday | 02:21 | 08:37 | 14:53 | 21:09 |
| Thursday | 03:25 | 09:41 | 15:57 | 22:13 |

**1.** What is the difference in time between the first high tide and the first low tide on each day? _____

**2.** What is the difference in time between the first high tide and the second high tide on each day? _____

**3.** What is the difference in time between the first high tide and the second low tide on each day? _____

**4.** What is the difference in time between the first high tide on one day and the first high tide on the next day?

_____

**5.** Write all the tide times for Friday, Saturday and Sunday.

Friday _____

Saturday _____

Sunday _____

**6.** What time is the last low tide on Saturday? _____

**7.** How many tides are there on

Watch out! When does Sunday morning start?

Friday? _____
Saturday? _____
Sunday? _____

**Teachers' note** Encourage the children to write down the times they are finding the difference between and to show their workings.

**Developing Numeracy
Solving Problems Year 6
© A & C Black**

**p 6**
1. $96 \cdot 9 - 9 \cdot 03$
2. $460 \cdot 4 - 72 \cdot 5$
3. $305 \cdot 1 \times 3 \cdot 1$
4. $6 \cdot 06 \div 40 \cdot 4$
5. $285 \cdot 4 + 3 \cdot 64$
6. $14 \cdot 3 \times 9 \cdot 74$
7. $1 \cdot 0000 \div 8 \cdot 0$
8. $122 \cdot 9 + 98 \cdot 3$
9. $300 \cdot 3 \times 9 \cdot 84$
There are other possible solutions to the multiplication and division statements.

**p 8**
Star = 22, circle = 2
Square = 9, triangle = 36
**Now try this!**
A = 9, B = 10

**p 9**
1. A = 6, B = 2
2. A = 12, B = 8
3. A = 25, B = 5
4. A = 5, B = 9
**Now try this!**
A = 2, B = 4, C = 1, D = 3, E = 5, F = 6

**p 10**
1. $102 \times 59$
2. $166 \times 37$
3. $222 \times 46$
4. $184 \times 54$
5. $799 \times 93$
6. $711 \times 13$
7. $336 \times 26$
8. $19 \times 41$
9. $344 \times 22$

**p 11**
1. 1050
2. 48
3. 80
4. 18 r 8 or $18\frac{2}{3}$ or $18 \cdot 6666$
5. 36
6. 1960
7. 39 r 3 or $39\frac{1}{3}$ or $39 \cdot 3333$

**p 12**
There are a variety of ways of arranging these dominoes, e.g.

**p 13**
**Now try this!**
This is one possible answer:
find 80% (80); divide by 2 (40); subtract 16 (24); find $\frac{3}{4}$ (18);
subtract 16 (2); divide by 2 (1).

**p 14**
| | | |
|---|---|---|
| 6, 7 | 8, 9 | 10, 11 |
| 14, 15 | 22, 23 | 24, 25 |
| 28, 29 | 34, 35 | 49, 50 |

**Now try this!**
| | | | |
|---|---|---|---|
| 10, 11 | 11, 12 | 12, 13 | 13, 14 |

**p 15**
| | | |
|---|---|---|
| 12, 13 | 15, 16 | 21, 22 |
| 27, 28 | 33, 34 | 42, 43 |
| 66, 67 | 82, 83 | 99, 100 |

**Now try this!**
| | | |
|---|---|---|
| 22, 23 | 23, 24 | 24, 25 |
| 25, 26 | 26, 27 | 27, 28 |
| 28, 29 | 29, 30 | 30, 31 |
| 31, 32 | | |

**p 16**
| | | | |
|---|---|---|---|
| 8 | 9 | 4 | 8 |
| 9 | 9 | 8 | 8 |
| | | | |
| 1 | 3 | 8 | |
| 7 | 3 | 9 | |

The following squares should be coloured yellow:
10–18, 20–27, 30–36, 40–45, 50–54, 60–63, 70–72, 80, 81, 90, 100
The following squares should be coloured red:
13, 22, 31, 40, 49, 58, 67, 76, 85, 94
The following squares should be coloured green:
18, 27, 36, 45, 54, 63, 72, 81, 90, 99

**p 17**
| | | |
|---|---|---|
| 6 | 1 | 4 |
| 5 | 2 | 3 |

Numbers that reduce to 2 in
one step: 11, 20, 101, 110, 200
two steps: 29, 38, 47, 56, 65, 74, 83, 92, 119, 128, 137, 146, 155, 164, 173, 182, 191

**Now try this!**
Numbers that reduce to 3 in
one step: 12, 21, 30, 102, 111, 120, 201, 210, 300
two steps: 39, 48, 57, 66, 75, 84, 93, 129, 138, 147, 156, 165, 174, 183, 192, 219, 228, 237, 246, 255, 264, 273, 282, 291

**p 18**
1. $\frac{1}{2} = 0 \cdot 5$
2. $\frac{7}{5} = 1 \cdot 4$
3. $\frac{5}{2} = 2 \cdot 5$
4. $\frac{9}{6} = 1 \cdot 5$
5. $\frac{6}{5} = 1 \cdot 2$
6. $\frac{6}{4} = 1 \cdot 5$
7. $\frac{3}{5} = 0 \cdot 6$ or $\frac{3}{6} = 0 \cdot 5$
8. $\frac{9}{5} = 1 \cdot 8$
9. $\frac{7}{2} = 3 \cdot 5$
10. $\frac{2}{5} = 0 \cdot 4$ or $\frac{2}{4} = 0 \cdot 5$

**Now try this!**
$\frac{3}{8} = 0 \cdot 375$

**p 19**
There are several solutions to these puzzles, e.g.

3. The dice can be arranged so that 7 dots are on one side and 21 on the other.
**Now try this!**
It is not possible to arrange 3 or 5 dice in the same way.

**p 20**
1.
| 4 | 1 | 5 |
|---|---|---|
| 8 | 7 | 2 |
| 3 | 6 | 9 |

2.
| 3 | 7 | 2 |
|---|---|---|
| 8 | 4 | 5 |
| 1 | 9 | 6 |

**p 21**
1.
| 8 | 7 | 2 |
|---|---|---|
| 4 | 3 | 6 |
| 1 | 5 | 9 |

2.
| 1 | 2 | 7 |
|---|---|---|
| 8 | 5 | 6 |
| 9 | 4 | 3 |

3.
| 6 | 8 | 1 |
|---|---|---|
| 2 | 4 | 9 |
| 7 | 3 | 5 |

**p 23**
1. 2756
2556
5088
2. 2332
2532
5088
3. 2850
2712
5472
4. 2622
2760
5472

**p 24**
1. twice as big
2. half as big
3. 10 times smaller
4. 10 times greater
5. four times larger
6. four times smaller

**p 25**
1. eight times greater
2. five times larger
3. five times smaller
4. nine times larger
5. three times bigger
6. four times smaller

**p 26**
1. $52 \times n$ **or** $52n$
2. $4 \times n$ **or** $4n$
3. $6 \times n$ **or** $6n$
4. $365 \times n$ **or** $365n$
5. $37 \times n$ **or** $37n$
**Now try this!**
$1440 \times n$ **or** $1440n$

**p 27**
1. $4 \times n$ **or** $4n$
   $1 \times n$ **or** $n$
   $5 \times n$ **or** $5n$
2. $2 \times n$ **or** $2n$
   $10 \times n$ **or** $10n$
   $10 \times n$ **or** $10n$

**p 28**
1. 7 people, 3 fish
2. 5 people, 2 dogs
3. 4 dogs, 1 fish
4. 5 people, 5 spiders
5. 4 people, 4 cats
6. 6 people, 8 dogs

**Now try this!**
3 fish, 4 people, 5 dogs

**p 29**
**1.** $8 + x$        **2.** $x \div 2$        **3.** $8 - x$        **4.** $x - 8$
**5.** $x - 2$        **6.** $2x$          **7.** $x + 2$

**Now try this!**
$x - y + z$

**p 30**
Names of quadrilaterals:

trapezium    rectangle    square    rhombus    kite

kite          parallelogram          trapezium

There are different solutions in the joined shapes, e.g.

**Now try this!**

**p 31**
Shapes formed with one straight line:
1 triangle and 1 trapezium
2 rectangles
2 squares
2 triangles
1 triangle and 1 pentagon
2 trapeziums
1 rectangle and 1 square

Shapes formed with two straight lines:
1 trapezium, 1 triangle, 1 rectangle
3 rectangles
1 rectangle, 2 triangles
1 rectangle, 1 pentagon, 1 triangle
1 rectangle, 1 trapezium, 1 triangle
3 triangles
2 triangles, 1 quadrilateral
2 triangles, 1 parallelogram
etc.

**p 32**

**p 33**

**Now try this!**

All the sides of a rhombus are equal.

**p 34**
**1.**

**2.**

**p 35**
**1.**

**2.**

**3.**

**p 36**
Yes, the angles in a triangle always add up to 180 degrees. It is unlikely that all the totals will be exactly 180 degrees due to inaccuracy of measuring.

**p 37**
Pick's theorem works for all shapes.

**p 39**
Missing numbers and fractions:

**1.**

| | |
|---|---|
| | $\frac{1}{24}$ |
| | $\frac{1}{12}$ |
| 6 | |
| | $\frac{1}{6}$ |
| 16 | $\frac{1}{3}$ |
| | $\frac{1}{2}$ |
| 36 | |

**2.**

| | |
|---|---|
| 3 | $\frac{1}{12}$ |
| 4 | $\frac{1}{9}$ |
| 6 | $\frac{1}{6}$ |
| 9 | $\frac{1}{4}$ |
| 18 | $\frac{1}{2}$ |
| 18 | |

**p 40**
**1.** 4
**2.** 40, 24, 52
**3.** Will depend upon present year.
**4.** Stockholm, Berlin
**5.** Will depend upon present year.

**Now try this!**
Cancelled games: 1916, 1940, 1944
Next 10 games: 2004, 2008, 2012, 2016, 2020, 2024, 2028, 2032, 2036, 2040

**p 41**
**1.** Points
72
67
57
57
55
53
49

**2.** 73        **3.** 58        **4.** 33
**5.** 3rd        **6.** 6        **7.** 1

**Now try this!**

| | | | | |
|---|---|---|---|---|
| Man Utd | 33 | 21 | 2 | 73 |
| Chelsea | 33 | 21 | 7 | 5 | 70 |
| Arsenal | 34 | 15 | 14 | 5 | 59 |
| Newcastle | 33 | 17 | 6 | 10 | 57 |
| Liverpool | 34 | 16 | 8 | 10 | 56 |
| Leeds | 34 | 14 | 13 | 7 | 55 |
| Aston Villa | 34 | 13 | 11 | 10 | 50 |

**p 42**

| | | | | | | |
|---|---|---|---|---|---|---|
| 560 | 373 | 464 | 116 | 58 | 174 | 264 |
| 232 | 448 | | | | | |

**p 43**

| | | | | | | |
|---|---|---|---|---|---|---|
| 480 | 368 | 345 | 115 | 230 | 23 | 322 |
| 30 | 315 | 177 | | | | |

**p 44**

| 1. | Nissan Micra | 4 mph | Ford Ka | 8 mph |
|---|---|---|---|---|
| | Ford Escort | 1 mph | VW Beetle | 12 mph |
| | BMW | 8 mph | Peugeot 106 | 20 mph |
| | Austin Mini | 10 mph | Ford Sierra | 9 mph |
| | Porsche | 7 mph | Honda Accord | 10 mph |
| | VW Golf | 12 mph | Renault Clio | 5 mph |
| | | | Toyota Corolla | 3 mph |

2. 6 mph, 10 mph
3. £200
4. £100   4
   £200   6
   £500   3

**Now try this!**
£3100

**p 45**
Prices could be given in pounds or pence.
1. 96p, 99p, 105p, 55p
2. 144p, 99p, 147p, 77p
3. 168p, 99p, 168p, 240p
4. 264p, 159p, 252p, 360p
5. 336p, 249p, 315p, 165p
If points are awarded for cheapness, scores are as follows:

| Cheap Talk | Talk for Less | Fast Chat | Quick Call |
|---|---|---|---|
| 3 | 2 | 1 | 4 |
| 2 | 3 | 1 | 4 |
| 3 | 4 | 3 | 1 |
| 2 | 4 | 3 | 1 |
| 1 | 3 | 2 | 4 |
| 11 | 16 | 10 | 14 |

Talk for Less is cheapest all round.

**p 46**
1. Lo Fare
2. Fly Cheap!
3. Cost Less
4. Fly Cheap!
5. Cost Less
6. Budget Buy!

**p 47**
1. Flight Savers!
2. Fare Deals
3. Best Buy!
4. Flight Savers!
5. Fare Deals
6. Lo Cost

**p 48**
1. £408 000
2. £416 000
3. £365 000
4. £438 000
5. £525 600
6. £315 360

**Now try this!**
Just over 3 years

**p 49**
1. 9 US Dollars
   1000 Japanese Yen
   7 Euros
   44 550 Zambia Kwacha
   148 750 Vietnam Dong
   264 Russian Rubles
2. 30p
   15.84 Russian Rubles
   0.42 Euros (42 cents)
   0.54 US Dollars (54 cents)
   8 925 Vietnam Dong
   2 673 Zambia Kwacha

**Now try this!**
21 250 Vietnam Dong

**p 51**
1. Areas:
   6900 m²
   10 920 m²
   364 m²
   5390 m²
   5017.86 m²
   1860.5 m²
   195.6271 m²
   463.6 m²
2. Football
3. Tennis
4. 4020 m²
5. 99.6 m²
6. 5530 m²
7. Basketball, tennis and netball

**p 52**
1. Table tennis, squash, tennis, cricket, football
2. Table tennis, squash, tennis, cricket, football
3. 56·37 g
4. 319 g
5. 4·88 oz
6. 16·911 oz
7. 31·7 mm
8. 0·13 inches

**Now try this!**
About 2·4 ounces
About 3·23 inches

**p 53**
1. Totals:  1425 g
            1362 g
            1412 g
            1440 g
            1397 g
            1360 g
            1310 g
2. 9706 g
3. 38 824 g
4. 504 700 g
5. Breakfast = 352 g
   Lunch = 481 g
   Evening meal = 553·6 g

**Now try this!**
An adult eats on average about 1 000 000 g per year, and a child about 500 000 g. Therefore, a 70-year life span (16 as a child, the rest as an adult) = 62 000 000 g – about the mass of 100 cars!

**p 54**
1. 1310 g
2. 71 g
3. 11 000 g
4. 30 g
5. 2·2 lb
6. 90 g
7. 3680 g

**Now try this!**
Approximately 12 kg

**p 55**
The following are all approximations:
1. 60 g
   150 g
   270 g
   240 g
   285 ml
2. 240 g
   960 g
   210 g
   120 g
   285 ml
3. 480 g
   210 g
   240 g
   960 g
   1140 ml or 1·140 l

**Now try this!**
teaspoon = 5 ml
tablespoon = 15 ml
114 teaspoons of water
38 tablespoons of water

**p 57**
1. 570 ml        0·57 l
   500 ml        ½ l
   1000 ml       1 l
   285 ml        0·285 l
2. 2355 ml       2·355 l
3. About 4 pints
4. Just more than a gallon

**Now try this!**
True
False
False
True
False (they are a lot more than 1 pint)

**p 58**
1. 2 hours 40 minutes
2. 20 minutes
3. 1 hour 40 minutes
4. 35 minutes
5. 4 hours 5 minutes
6. 5, 10

**p 59**
1. 1 hour 43 minutes
2. 1 hour 17 minutes
3. 2 hours 8½ minutes
4. 37 minutes
5. 4 hours 19 minutes
6. 4, 9

**p 60**
1. 6 hours 16 minutes
   6 hours 16 minutes
   6 hours 16 minutes
   They are all the same.
2. 6 hours 16 minutes
3. 6 hours 16 nutes
4. Friday        04:32    10:48    17:04    23:20

**Now try this!**
Saturday      05:36    11:52    18:08
Sunday        00:24    06:40    12:56    19:12

**p 61**
1. 6 hours 16 minutes
2. 12 hours 32 minutes
3. 18 hours 48 minutes
4. 25 hours 4 minutes
5. Friday        04:29    10:45    17:01    23:17
   Saturday      05:33    11:49    18:05
   Sunday        00:21    06:37    12:53    19:09
6. 11:49
7. 4, 3, 4